STATISTICS IN ACTION
Book 2
DISTRIBUTION THEORY

STATISTICS IN ACTION
Book 2
DISTRIBUTION THEORY

Peter J. Dolton PhD
Computer Co-ordinator, Bristol University

Gerald H. Makepeace
Lecturer in Economics, University of Hull

John G. Treble PhD
Senior Lecturer in Economics, University of Hull

McGRAW-HILL BOOK COMPANY

London · New York · St Louis · San Francisco · Auckland · Bogotá · Guatemala
Hamburg · Lisbon · Madrid · Mexico · Montreal · New Delhi · Panama · Paris
San Juan · São Paulo · Singapore · Sydney · Tokyo · Toronto

Published by
McGRAW-HILL Book Company (UK) Limited
MAIDENHEAD · BERKSHIRE · ENGLAND

British Library Cataloguing in Publication Data

Dolton, Peter J.
  Statistics in action.
  Bk. 2: Distribution theory
  1. Statistical mathematics. Applications
  of microcomputer systems. Software packages
  I. Title   II. Makepeace, Gerald H.
  III. Treble, John G.
  519.5'028'5536
  ISBN 0-07-707113-1

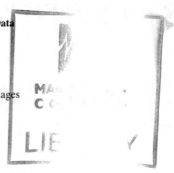

Library of Congress Cataloging-in-Publication Data

Dolton, Peter J.
  Statistics in action/Peter J. Dolton, Gerald H. Makepeace,
  John G. Treble.
    p.   cm.
  Includes bibliographies and indexes.
  Contents: bk. 1. Descriptive statistics—bk. 2. Distribution
  theory—bk. 3. Estimation and inference.
  ISBN 0-07-707113-1
  1. Mathematical statistics. I. Makepeace, Gerald H.
  II. Treble, John. III. Title.
  QA276D64   1989
  519.5—dc19   88-13348

1234 AP 9089

Typeset by Best-set Typesetter Limited
Printed and bound in Great Britain by The Alden Press, Oxford

In memory of
Carol Makepeace

CONTENTS

* indicates more advanced or specialized material

PREFACE

Statistics in Action began as a few demonstration programs that one of the authors experimented with almost a decade ago. In those days before the great microcomputer revolution, such activities had to be mounted on a mainframe computer, time had to be found for students to run the programs and the response via a lineprinter was neither quick nor convenient. The effort involved in running the first of these programs (a later version of which appears in *Statistics in Action, Book 3* as the interactive central limit theorem program) was quite substantial in administrative terms.

For many schools, colleges and universities the coming of the microcomputer has changed all this. Equipment is now sufficiently cheap for classes commonly to have access to one machine for each one or two students, and the flexibility permitted by interactive working enables individual students to use programs of the sort presented here, working at their own pace, and without recourse to paper output.

Despite the widespread availability of computer hardware, computer software for use in courses is still quite hard to come by. This realization, and the enthusiasm of a potential publisher, encouraged the three of us to embark on the task of producing a suite of programs that would cover a large part of the A-level syllabus in statistics, and also the material that we ourselves had each been teaching to first year Economics students at the University of Hull. Had we realized at the outset how large a task we had set ourselves, it is doubtful whether simple enthusiasm on the part of the publisher would have been sufficient to induce us to start! We quickly discovered that the coordination of text and graphics to produce a smoothly flowing exposition is by no means simple and that the production of interactive programs that are interesting, fast and foolproof is an art that none of us knew existed until we attempted it ourselves.

Anyone who has tried to explain to a class of students what a random variable is, or what is meant by 'consistency', or why the arithmetic mean is sensitive to outliers using only conventional, static apparatus, will know that these are rather difficult ideas to get across. In our programs, we have selected as topics for special attention those parts of the elementary syllabus that we thought would gain most from a dynamic treatment on the small screen. Thus the distribution function unfolds as the area under the density function before your very eyes, and becomes readily comprehensible, even if you did not quite follow all the integral signs on the blackboard. Distributions of estimators can be plotted quickly and easily, so that the advantages of large samples can readily be appreciated (and perhaps the fact that 'large' is not quite as big as you thought). Many other examples could be mentioned of difficult concepts that can be brought to life by the use of the microcomputer as a teaching aid. Rather than listing them here, we would urge you to look for yourselves.

The programs are written mainly with two groups of students in mind: students who are preparing for GCE at A level and students in a first year university or polytechnic course for non-specialist statisticians. All these courses will contain coverage of descriptive statistics. They will all provide some introduction to probability theory, and the basic ideas and methods of statistical inference. Whether they will all cover the Lorenz curve and the Gini coefficient, or the asymptotic properties of estimators, we rather doubt. Where we have thought the material more advanced or perhaps a little specialized, we have asterisked the Section in the text.

The material is organized into three separate books, each of which is self-contained and is accompanied (optionally) by the relevant software. Book 1 deals with *Descriptive Statistics*, Book 2 is concerned with *Distribution Theory* and Book 3 covers *Estimation and Inference*.

The books are not intended to be a substitute for a full-blown textbook, but are designed to put the salient information forward and, where the software is available, to be a guide to the programs and put them into context. In addition, there is some material which can be more effectively conveyed through the medium of the printed page. Conversely, much of the software can be appreciated and practised without reference to the accompanying text. The complete package, however, most effectively combines the advantages of print and electronic media.

Appendix A provides a brief description of the software associated with this volume, and Appendix C summarizes the software from the complete package.

ACKNOWLEDGEMENTS

The job of bringing a three-author project to fruition is not an easy one. We would like to acknowledge the enthusiasm of Philip Allan, who first encouraged us to expand our early efforts to a book/multidisk package, and also of Gareth Mallet and Jon Finegold, without whose cheerfulness and faith *Statistics in Action* would never have seen the light of day. The software has been tried out on several classes of students at the University of Hull and Newland High School, Hull. Our thanks are due to the students and the teachers involved. In addition, a number of our colleagues at the Universities of Hull and Bristol have, on occasion, given freely of their time and critical acumen. Tim Barmby, Ian Davidson, Steve Trotter, Geoff Whittington and Laurie Burbridge have been particularly generous in this respect.

ABBREVIATIONS AND NOTATION

DISTRIBUTIONS

χ^2	chi-squared distribution
$U[a,b]$	uniform distribution with range a to b
$b(n,p)$	binomial distribution with parameters n and p
$p(\lambda)$	Poisson distribution with parameter λ
$e(\lambda)$	exponential distribution with parameter λ
$N(\mu, \sigma^2)$	normal distribution with mean μ and variance σ^2
$\Gamma(\lambda, \alpha)$	gamma distribution with parameters λ and α
$\beta(a,b)$	beta distribution with parameters a and b
$t(n)$	Student's-t distribution with n degrees of freedom

SCIENTIFIC

$a \times b, ab$	Cartesian product of a and b
$\cap$	intersection of
$\cup$	union of
$'$	the complement of
$\subset$	subset of
$\not\subset$	not a subset of
$\in$	element of
$\notin$	not an element of
$\varnothing$	the null set
$\{x; \ldots\}$	the set of x such that

$\mathbb{Z}$	the set of integers
$\mathbb{R}$	the set of real numbers
$\lvert X \rvert$	absolute value of X
$x!$	factorial x
$=$	equal to
$\simeq$	approximately equal to
$\equiv$	equal by definition
$<$	less than
$>$	greater than
$\leqslant$	no greater than
$\geqslant$	no less than
$\int_a^b f(x)\mathrm{d}x$	integral of $f(x)$ over the range a to b
$\nparallel$	break in the values represented by a line
$\frac{\mathrm{d}f(.)}{\mathrm{d}x}$	first derivative of univariate function f with respect to x
$\frac{\partial f(.)}{\partial x}$	first partial derivative of multivariate function f with respect to x
$\mathrm{B}(a, b)$	beta function where $\mathrm{B}(a, b) = \int_0^1 x^{a-1}(1-x)^{b-1}\mathrm{d}x$
$\Gamma(\lambda)$	gamma function where $\Gamma(\mathrm{t}) = \int_0^\infty \mathrm{e}^{-y}y^{\lambda-1}\mathrm{d}y$

OTHER

A	intercept of the true regression model
B	slope of the true regression model
a	intercept of the estimated regression model
b	slope of the estimated regression model
C_i	width of the ith class
CV	coefficient of variation
cf_i	cumulative frequency of the ith class
c.d.f.	cumulative distribution function
c.r.f.	cumulative relative frequency
c.r.f.$_i$	cumulative relative frequency of the ith class
e_i	error or deviation of a data value from some fixed value (Chapter 2, Book 1), estimated error in a regression model

f_i	frequency of the ith class
GC	Gini coefficient
H_0	the null hypothesis
H_1	the alternative hypothesis
IR	interquartile range
j.p.f.	joint probability function
j.c.d.f.	joint cumulative distribution function
j.p.d.f.	joint probability density function
K	measure of kurtosis
$L(.)$	likelihood function
LCL_i	actual lower class limit of the ith class
LR	likelihood ratio
lim	limit of
M_r	rth moment of a set of data
m.p.d.f.	marginal probability density function
n	the sample size
$P(.)$	probability of
$P(y\|x)$	probability of y conditional on x
p.d.f.	probability density function
p.f.	probability function
Q_i	ith quartile
R^2	the coefficient of determination
r	the sample correlation coefficient
r.v.	random variable
S	space or sample space
s^2	sample variance
s_2^2	unbiased estimator of the variance of the errors in a regression model
s.e.(a)	standard error of a
s.e.(b)	standard error of b
UCL_i	actual upper class limit of the ith class
u_i	true error in a regression model
$X_1, \ldots, X_n$	values of X in a sample
$\overline{X}$	the sample mean
z	z score or standardized normal deviate
μ	mean of a random variable
ϱ	correlation coefficient
σ	standard deviation of a random variable
σ^2	variance of a random variable
φ	p.d.f. of the normal distribution
Φ	c.d.f. of the normal distribution
$\sum_{i=1}^{n} X_i$	the sum of $X_1, X_2, \ldots, X_n$,

AN INTRODUCTION TO PROBABILITY

1.1 INTRODUCTION

The probability of an event is a number that takes a value between 0 and 1. This number expresses the likelihood of that event occurring. Therefore a probability of 0 relates to the total impossibility of an event taking place and a probability of 1 corresponds to complete certainty. A value of .5 indicates that an event is equally likely to occur or not to occur. In general the closer is the probability to zero the less likely the event is to occur. In this chapter we will develop the laws that govern the behaviour of probabilities and their interrelation.

There are many phrases that are used in everyday language to express intuitively the notion of the likelihood of an event. When we use such words as likely or rarely, do we always mean the same thing? Even more interesting; do different people mean different things when using the same phrase? Two psychologists (Lichtenstein and Newman) gave a questionnaire referring to many words and phrases to a large number of people and asked each person to attach the probability number between 0 and 1 that most clearly reflected the degree of probability implied by each word or phrase. In Table 1.1 some of Lichtenstein and Newman's results are reproduced. These are better consulted after using Program 4. The results reported by Lichtenstein and Newman (1967) were obtained by surveying 184 people. For each word or phrase the mean, median, standard deviation and the range from this sample are tabulated. If you use Program 4 you can compare your perceptions with those in the sample. This program presents a graphical display of the descriptive statistics summarizing the response of

Table 1.1 Words and probability

Word or phrase	Mean	Median	σ	Range
Very likely	.87	.90	.04	.60–.99
Rather unlikely	.24	.25	.12	.01–.75
Fighting chance	.47	.50	.17	.05–.90
Not very probable	.20	.20	.12	.01–.60
Toss-up	.50	.50	.01	.45–.52
Somewhat unlikely	.31	.33	.12	.03–.08
Possible	.37	.49	.23	.01–.99
Quite unlikely	.11	.10	.08	.01–.05
Good chance	.74	.75	.12	.25–.96
Likely	.72	.75	.11	.25–.99
Highly probable	.89	.90	.04	.60–.99
Fairly likely	.66	.70	.12	.15–.95
Uncertain	.40	.50	.14	.08–.90
Probable	.71	.75	.17	.01–.99
Very unlikely	.09	.10	.07	.01–.50
Highly improbable	.06	.05	.05	.01–.30
Rather likely	.69	.70	.09	.15–.99
Very probable	.87	.89	.07	.60–.99
Usually	.77	.75	.13	.15–.99
Barely possible	.13	.05	.17	.01–.60
Improbable	.12	.10	.09	.01–.40
Quite likely	.79	.80	.10	.30–.99
Fairly unlikely	.25	.25	.11	.02–.75
Somewhat likely	.59	.60	.18	.20–.92
Fair chance	.51	.50	.13	.20–.85
Rare	.07	.05	.07	.01–.30

Source: Lichtenstein and Newman (1967).

people in the sample and includes the range of two standard deviations either side of the population mean. Such a $\pm 2\sigma$ range shows the range of values given by more than 75 per cent of people.

Exercises 1.1

These questions should be attempted after using Program 4.

Exercise 1.1.1 What did you notice about Lichtenstein and Newman's (1976) results? Was the sample mean usually close to the median?

Exercise 1.1.2 Did the presence of a qualifying word or phrase, e.g. very, rather, etc., increase the $\mu \pm 2\sigma$ range?

Exercise 1.1.3 Was your assessment usually close to μ and the median?

Exercise 1.1.4 Would you attach the same probabilities to the same phrase in two different contexts? For example consider:
(a) There is a *fair chance* that the sun will shine tomorrow.
(b) The doctor says that the operation has a *fair chance* of success.

1.2 PROBABILITY AS A RELATIVE FREQUENCY AND A DEGREE OF BELIEF

The issue of what is meant by the concept of 'probability' is a complex problem in philosophy. Broadly there are two main schools of thought: *frequentist* (or classical school) and *Bayesian*. The frequentist notion of probability suggests that probability is a relative frequency that occurs in the world. The Bayesian view is that probability is a (subjective) degree of belief about the world.

To suggest that a head has probability ½ of occurring when a coin is tossed, because approximately 500 occurrences in 1000 trials have been observed, is a frequentist notion. Therefore such a concept relies on the relative frequency of an event when considered as a proportion of a large number of trials.

To further explore the frequentist notion of probability you can use Program 5 to simulate the tossing of a fair coin. In this program you will be asked the number of tosses you wish to simulate and the computer will graph the relative proportion of heads that occur. The graphs for simulating 15 tosses and 1000 tosses may look something like those in Fig. 1.1. (They may, however, look different on the computer since each run of the program provides a unique simulation.)

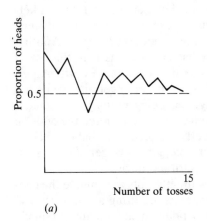

(a)

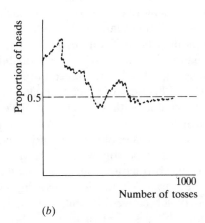

(b)

Figure 1.1

Exercises 1.2

These questions should be attempted after using Program 5.

Exercise 1.2.1 What happens to the relative frequency as the number of trials increase? Why should this occur?

Exercise 1.2.2 Explain why, even at a fairly large number of trials, the convergence to the .5 proportion may not be monotonic. (In other words, why is it possible for the proportion to diverge momentarily away from .5 even at the thousandth trial?) [A good reference on such simulations is Feller (1968, chap. III).]

Since many events cannot be repeated under controlled conditions this notion of probability is not applicable to all situations. To believe that the Chicago Bears have a one in four chance of winning the Super Bowl this season cannot be based on a large number of repetitions and must be a subjective view.

Subjective probability is a personal evaluation of the likelihood of a chance phenomenon. Keynes (1921) and Jeffreys (1939) suggested this view of probability as an alternative to the frequentist concept. More specifically, this notion is important in the development of Bayesian decision theory. Essentially, subjective probability requires the judgement of an individual that the likelihood of an event is defined to be a number ranging from 0 to 1. This probability value may have nothing to do with the frequency of occurrence in a large number of trials but may simply be a subjective evaluation of the likelihood of a single event. Such a notion is therefore useful in non-repeatable experiments. Other situations in which it could be useful to use a subjective notion is when events to be compared can only be judged as more or less likely than each other. For example, it is more likely that it will rain tomorrow than that the sun will shine. Such ordinal evaluations may be difficult to quantify in relative numerical terms. Another situation in which subjective probability has applications is in the use of money and betting to ascertain the likelihood of uncertain events. A person's willingness to place a monetary evaluation on uncertain events has a direct link with subjective probability; i.e. being prepared to stake a specified amount of money on an uncertain event when quoted the odds on that event by a bookmaker is indicative of the subjective probability beliefs held by the person who is prepared to accept that wager. (This is, of course, abstracting from that individual's attitude to risk.)

Program 6 in the accompanying software attempts to simulate the concept of subjective probability. Imagine that you are firing a gun which will always hit a square of unit size but each point in the square is equally likely to be hit. You are aiming to hit a lighted area inside this unit square;

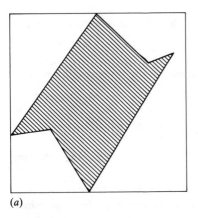

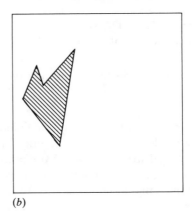

(a)   (b)

Figure 1.2

however, you have no control over the direction of the gun (except that it will always hit somewhere inside the unit square.) What then will be the probabilities of hitting the shaded areas in the squares shown above in Fig. 1.2a and b?

Many other similar examples are presented at random in Program 6. We strongly suggest that you try the program before you proceed to the next section.

Exercises 1.2 (*continued*)

What difficulties did you experience in trying to evaluate the areas and probabilities?

Exercise 1.2.3 Did you find that your evaluation was different from someone else who may have been viewing the same area? The guessing of areas and probabilities is subjective.

Exercise 1.2.4 Did certain shapes provide an optical illusion? (This may be analogous to how deceptive the evaluation of certain events may be.)

Exercise 1.2.5 Was the evaluation of small areas and probabilities particularly difficult?

Exercise 1.2.6 Did you find the accuracy of your evaluations gradually improved? (This may be analogous to a learning process which could occur in the assessment of similiar chance events.)

Do some more evaluations, keeping a record of your guess and the actual value of the area, and see if these effects occur.

Exercise 1.2.7 Do your results have any value in the assessment of the subjective probability notion?

Finally, consider some questions relating to the construction of this program:

1. How might the shape of the lighted area be drawn in order to represent a random area inside the unit square?
2. What distribution would you prefer to see on these areas if the program was run a large number of times?
3. Given that a shape has been drawn in the unit square on the screen how might you evaluate its relative size in order to compute the probability to be reported on the screen? (It is indeed ironic that the most straightforward method of doing this is to count the relative frequency of the lighted pixels.)

In the literature on probability there is a considerable debate over the use, appropriateness and validity of the frequentist and subjective notions of probability. Unfortunately this introductory exposition must pass over these issues. One point should, however, be made clearly; whichever notion of probability is used the laws of probability and the theory that will be studied in this text remain the same. (Whether an individual who holds subjective probability views is logically consistent may be another matter.)

Exercises 1.2 (*continued*)

Exercise 1.2.8 How would you assign a probability to the following events?
   (*a*) A six occurring in the throw of a fair die
   (*b*) A six occurring in the throw of a die of unknown characteristics
   (*c*) The probability of a horse winning a race
   (*d*) Two heads occurring in two throws of a fair coin
   (*e*) It snows on the first day of the next cricket season
   (*f*) An extraterrestrial arriving on earth
   (*g*) The Chicago Bears winning the next Super Bowl
   (*h*) Sighting a UFO on your way home tomorrow night

1.3 SET THEORY

Elementary set theory is a prerequisite for a study of probability theory. Many of the concepts in set theory can be illustrated diagrammatically using Venn diagrams. This approach is adopted in Programs 1, 2 and 3 and in this section after introducing some elementary concepts.

Definition 1.3.1 A *set* is a collection of items.

For example, the whole numbers (positive integers) between 1 and 6 may comprise the set; let us call it A. This is a convenient set to use since it is also the possible outcomes of tossing a die.

Definition 1.3.2 The items comprising a set are called *elements*, e.g. if x is an element of set A we write

$$x \in A$$

For example, 3 is an element of the set of positive integers (denoted by $\mathbb{Z}$) from 1 to 6; therefore 3 is an element of the set A.

If y is not in the set A we write

$$y \notin A$$

For example, the number 3.01 is a real number between 1 and 6 but not an integer; therefore it is not in the set A. Likewise 9 is an integer but also not in our set A since it is larger than 6.

Definition 1.3.3 The *null* set, $\varnothing$, is the set with no elements.

For example, the set of all integers less than 1 but greater than 0 has no elements, i.e. it is an empty set and would be an example of a null set.

Definition 1.3.4 If every element of A belongs to a set B then A is a *subset* of B, that is $A \subset B$.

$$\Rightarrow \text{ if } x \in A \text{ then } x \in B$$

If a set D is not a subset of B we can write this as $D \not\subset B$.

For example, if B_1 is the set of integers from 1 to 10 then A is obviously contained in B_1, that is $A \subset B_1$. Likewise, if B_2 is the set of all real numbers from 1 to 6 then A would still be a subset of B_2, that is $A \subset B_2$. (Note that $B_1 \not\subset B_2$ and $B_2 \not\subset B_1$.)

Often all the elements of a set cannot be listed or listing them individually is tedious, that is

$$A = (1, 2, 3, 4, 5, 6)$$

Hence the following notation is used

$$A = \{x; \ldots\}$$

where what follows the semicolon gives the property that puts x in A. Such notation is read 'the set of x such that'.

For the sets previously defined we may write

$$A = \{x; 1 \leq x \leq 6, x \in \mathbb{Z}\}$$
$$B_1 = \{x; 1 \leq x \leq 10, x \in \mathbb{Z}\}$$
$$B_2 = \{x; 0 \leq x \leq 6, x \in \mathbb{R}\}$$

where $\mathbb{Z}$ denotes the set of all positive integers and $\mathbb{R}$ the set of all real numbers.

Definition 1.3.5 A is a *proper subset* of B if

$$A \subset B \text{ and } A \neq B$$

Note that $A = B$ iff (if and only if) $A \subset B$ and $B \subset A$.

Definition 1.3.6 The largest set (relevant to a particular problem) of which all other sets are subsets is the *space*, S, or *universal* set U.

It is helpful to illustrate concepts in set theory by Venn diagrams; e.g. let S be the box in Fig. 1.3. Conceptually this must be thought of as a set so large as to contain all possible subsets. An example might be to consider the universal set to be the set of all numbers. In such a universal set real numbers and integers are only subsets (e.g. there is also another kind of number called a complex number which would also be in the set of all numbers).

Figure 1.3

Definition 1.3.7 The *union*, $\cup$, of two sets is the set of elements that belong to either A or B (Fig. 1.4), that is

$$A \cup B = \{x; x \in A \text{ or } x \in B\}$$

For example, if $B = \{x; 1 \leq x \leq 3, x \in \mathbb{R}\}$ and $A = \{x; 1 \leq x \leq 6, x \in \mathbb{Z}\}$ then

$$A \cup B = \{x; 1 \leq x \leq 6, x \in \mathbb{Z} \text{ or } 1 \leq x \leq 3, x \in \mathbb{R}\}$$

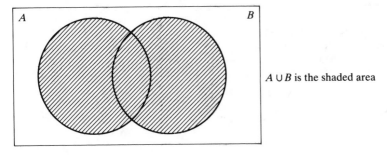

$A \cup B$ is the shaded area

Figure 1.4

An alternative diagram may represent these sets on the real line, that is

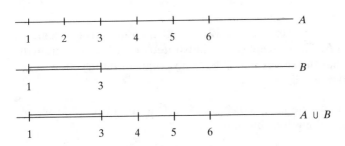

Definition 1.3.8 The *intersection*, ∩, of two sets is the set of elements that belong to *A and B* (Fig. 1.5) (the notation AB is sometimes used to denote $A \cap B$), so that

$$A \cap B = \{x; x \in A \text{ and } x \in B\}$$

Therefore, in our example above

$$A \cap B = \{1, 2, 3\} \text{ or } A \cap B = \{x; 1 \leqslant x \leqslant 3, x \in \mathbb{Z}\}$$

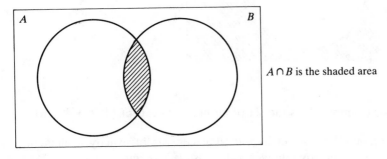

$A \cap B$ is the shaded area

Figure 1.5

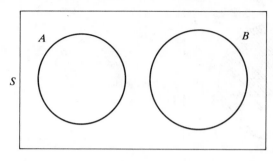

Figure 1.6

Definition 1.3.9 Two sets are *disjoint* or *mutually exclusive* if they have no elements in common, so that their intersection is the null set:

$$A \cap B = \varnothing$$

For example, if $B = \{x; 7 \leqslant x \leqslant 12, x \in \mathbb{Z}\}$ then there is no element in A that is also in B. The concept can be illustrated in the Venn diagram in Fig. 1.6. Notice that the sets A and B have no points of intersection since they do not overlap at all.

Definition 1.3.10 The *complement* of A, A' or A^c, in S is the set of elements that belong to S but not to A:

$$A^c = A' = \{x; x \notin A\}$$

In the Venn diagram in Fig. 1.7 the complement of A is everything outside A but contained in S.

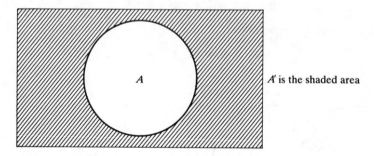

A' is the shaded area

Figure 1.7

In our example A' is the set of all numbers except $\{1, 2, 3, 4, 5, 6\}$.

Definition 1.3.11 A set is *finite* if it consists of exactly n elements, where n is a positive integer; otherwise it is *infinite*.

The set A in our examples is a finite set since there are a countable number of elements in the set, that is 6. (Countability is not a sufficient condition for a set to be finite. The set of real numbers is not countable since it is impossible to list all its elements. (Any interval of the real line is also infinite and not countable since there is an arbitrarily large number of values that can be taken by a real number in the interval.) The set of real numbers is also said to be unbounded since there always exists a number at least one larger than any we can think of.

Definition 1.3.12 The *Cartesian product* of A and B, $A \times B$ is

$$A \times B = \{(a,b); a \in A, b \in B\}$$

i.e. the set of every conceivable ordered pair.

If B in this example was the set

$$B = \{y; 1 \leq y \leq 6, y \in \mathbb{Z}\}$$

then $A \times B$ could be visualized as the lattice of 36 points in x, y space given in Fig. 1.8.

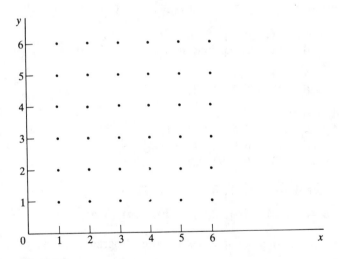

Figure 1.8

Theorem 1.3.1 *Laws of algebra of sets.* The following statements concerning sets are all true and may be verified by the use of Venn diagrams. This verification can easily be done by using Program 3.

Idempotent law
1a. $A \cup A = A$ 1b. $A \cap A = A$

Associative law
2a. $(A \cup B) \cup C = A \cup (B \cup C)$
2b. $(A \cap B) \cap C = A \cap (B \cap C)$
Commutative law
3a. $A \cap B = B \cap A$ 3b. $A \cup B = B \cup A$
Distributive law
4a. $A \cup (B \cap C) = (A \cup B) \cap (A \cup C)$
4b. $A \cap (B \cup C) = (A \cap B) \cup (A \cap C)$
Identity laws
5a. $A \cup \emptyset = A$ 5b. $A \cap U = A$
6a. $A \cup U = U$ 6b. $A \cap \emptyset = \emptyset$
Complement laws
7a. $A \cup A' = U$ 7b. $A \cap A' = \emptyset$
8a. $(A')' = A$ 8b. $U' = \emptyset, \emptyset' = U$
De Morgan's laws
9a. $(A \cup B)' = A' \cap B'$ 9b. $(A \cap B)' = A' \cup B'$

The examples below illustrate many of the concepts introduced in this section.

Example 1.3.1 Let U now be the set of integers and

$$A = \{x; x \text{ is an odd integer}, x < 10\}$$
$$B = \{x; x \text{ is a prime number}, x < 15\}$$

Then
$$A = \{1, 3, 5, 7, 9\}$$
$$B = \{2, 3, 5, 7, 11, 13\}$$

and
$$A \cap B = \{3, 5, 7\}$$
$$A \cup B = \{1, 2, 3, 5, 7, 9, 11, 13\}$$
$$A' = \{2, 4, 6, 8, 10, 11, 12, \ldots\}$$
$$B' = \{1, 4, 6, 8, 9, 10, 12, 14, \ldots\}$$

Example 1.3.2 Let $A = \{1, 2, 3\}$, $B = \{a, b\}$. Then

$$A \times B = \{(1, a), (1, b), (2, a), (2, b), (3, a), (3, b)\}$$

Example 1.3.3 (This is the example described in Program 2.) Let

$$U = \{(x, y); 1 \leq x, y \leq 6, x, y \in \mathbb{R}\}$$
$$A = \{(x, y); 1 \leq x, y \leq 6, x, y \in \mathbb{Z}\}$$

Let points in A be denoted by a dot (.) in Fig. 1.9.

$$B = \{(x, y); 1 \leq x, y \leq 6, x, y \in P\}$$

Let points in B be denoted by a cross ($\times$) in Fig. 1.9.

$$C = \{(x, y); x + y = 5, x, y \in \mathbb{Z}\}$$

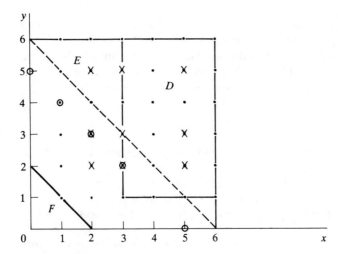

Figure 1.9

Let points in C be denoted by a circle ($\circ$) in Fig. 1.9.

$$D = \{(x,y); x \geqslant 3, y \geqslant 1\}$$
$$E = \{(x,y); x+y \geqslant 6\}$$
$$F = \{(x,y); x+y \leqslant 2\}$$

where P denotes the set of prime numbers and $\mathbb{Z}$ denotes the set of integers.

Let $A_x = \{x; 1 \leqslant x \leqslant 6, x \in \mathbb{Z}\}$
and $A_y = \{y; 1 \leqslant y \leqslant 6, y \in \mathbb{Z}\}$
  Then the *Cartesian product* of $A_x \times A_y$ is the set A, that is

$$A = A_x \times A_y = \{(x,y); 1 \leqslant x,y \leqslant 6, x,y \in \mathbb{Z}\}$$

The *union* of the sets B and C is the set of all points marked by $\circ$ or $\times$, that is

$$B \cup C = \{(0,5),(1,4),(2,3),(3,2),(4,1),(5,0),(2,2),(3,3),$$
$$(2,5),(3,5),(5,2),(5,3),(5,5)\}$$

The *intersection* of sets B and C is the set of all points marked by *both* a $\circ$ and a $\times$, that is

$$B \cap C = \{(2,3),(3,2)\}$$

Both sets B and C are contained in set A and are therefore subsets of A, that is

$$B \subset A, \qquad C \subset A$$

Sets E and F are *disjoint* or *mutually exclusive* because they do not overlap or have elements in common.

The *complement* of E, that is E', is the area below the line $x + y = 6$. That is all the points not in E.

Note that the sets A, B and C are *finite* sets since they have a finite number of elements. The sets D, E and F are *infinite* sets since they all have an arbitarily large possible number of elements.

Exercises 1.3

Exercise 1.3.1 Find the union $A \cup B$ and the intersection $A \cap B$ of the two sets A and B where:

(a) $A = \{x; x = 1, 2, 3\}$,　$B = \{x; x = 0, 1, 4\}$
(b) $A = \{x; 0 < x < 4\}$,　$B = \{x; 2 \leqslant x \leqslant 6\}$
(c) $A = \{(x, y); 0 < x, y < 3\}$,　$B = \{(x, y); 2 < x, y < 5\}$

Exercise 1.3.2 Let $A = \{(x, y), x, y \in \mathbb{Z}^{>0}\}$, that is let A be the set of points in x, y space that are positive integers. Let F be the number of points in A. Find $A_1 \cap A_2$, $F(A_1)$ and $F(A_2)$ where

$$A_1 = \{(x, y); x^2 + y^2 \leqslant 4\}$$
$$A_2 = \{(x, y); 0 \leqslant x, y \leqslant 3\}$$

Exercise 1.3.3 For the sets in Example 1.3.3 find:

(a) $A \cap B$
(b) $A \cap B \cup C$
(c) $D \cap A$
(d) $D \cap C$

Draw a diagram of:

(e) $E \cup D$
(f) $E' \cap D$

Exercise 1.3.4 Consider the sets:

$A = \{$all people with 'full blown' AIDS$\}$
$B = \{$all people with the HIV virus$\}$
$Q = \{$all homosexuals$\}$
$D = \{$all drug abusers$\}$
$H = \{$all haemophiliacs$\}$
$M = \{$all men$\}$
$W = \{$all women$\}$
$N = \{$chaste nuns and other lifetime sexual abstainers$\}$
$P = \{$all sexual partners of people with the HIV virus$\}$

(a) Describe the sets $A \cap B$, $N \cap M$, $H \cup P$, $(Q \cup A) \cap M$, $D \cap M$.

(b) Is $A \subset M$?
　　$A \subset Q$?

$$(A \cap M) \subset Q?$$
$$A \subset H?$$
$$P \subset H?$$

(c) Define precisely, in terms of these sets, those people who have the most chance of catching AIDS.

(d) Using these sets can you explain some of the early prejudices regarding the people who first caught this disease?

Exercise 1.3.5 Using Program 3:
(a) Verify De Morgan's laws.
(b) Simplify the following expressions:
  (i) $(A \cap B)' \cap A$
  (ii) $(A \cup B) \cap B'$
  (iii) $(A \cup C) \cap (A \cup B)$
  (iv) $((A \cap B) \cup B)'$
  (v) $(A \cap B) \cup (A \cap C)$
  (vi) $[((A \cup B)' \cap C) \cup ((A \cup C)' \cap B) \cup ((B \cup C)' \cap A)]'$
(c) Verify the laws of sets given in Theorem 1.3.1.

Exercise 1.3.6 Consider the whole female population. Define A as the set of all women over 25, B as the set of all divorcees and C as all mothers. What is the set theory expression for:
(a) All women without children
(b) All women who are divorced or have children
(c) Divorced women under 25
(d) Women who are neither divorced, nor mothers and are under 25
(e) Mothers over 25 who are not divorced
Use Program 3 to depict each of these sets.

1.4 COMBINATORIAL ANALYSIS

Combinatorial analysis is a method of determining the number of elements in a particular set without the direct enumeration of all the elements individually, i.e. combinatorial analysis makes it easier to count the number of elements in a set. Two of the programs in the accompanying software relate to this section: Program 7 describes the concepts in this section and Program 11 enables you to perform your own combinatorial calculations easily.

To illustrate the principles involved in basic counting procedures we may revert to our example earlier in this chapter. Consider again that A and B are the set of integers from 1 to 6, that is

$$A = \{x; 1 \leq x \leq 6, x \in \mathbb{Z}\}$$
$$B = \{y; 1 \leq y \leq 6, y \in \mathbb{Z}\}$$

Now suppose that we are interested in counting the distinct pairs (x, y) of elements that can be formed by selecting first an element from A and then an element from B. There are six ways of taking an element from A. For each of them, there are, in turn, six ways of taking an element from B. Hence there are 36 distinct pairs of (x, y) each containing one element from A and one from B. Indeed, this corresponds to the lattice of points in two-dimensional space $(\mathbb{R}^2)$ which was represented in Fig. 1.8.

To generalize these observations from counting over two sets to counting over k sets with $n_1, n_2, n_3, n_4, \ldots, n_k$ elements is straightforward. First we count the number of elements in the first set, n_1, and then multiply this by the number in the second set, n_2, since for each chosen element in the first set there are n_2 ways of choosing the element in the second set. This in turn would be multiplied by n_3, the number of elements in the third set, since for each pair so far enumerated there are n_3 ways of choosing a third component from the third set. This logic is then repeated over the k sets. More formally the principle of counting can be stated as follows:

Definition 1.4.1 *Fundamental principle of counting.* If a first procedure can be performed n_1 different ways, a second procedure in n_2 different ways, and so forth, then the total number of ways the procedures can be performed (in the order indicated) is

$$n_1 n_2 n_3 \cdots$$

Example 1.4.1 How many different possible motor vehicle licence plates are there in the United Kingdom under the present system?

Each number plate begins with a letter (excluding Q, I, U and Z), followed by three numbers (excluding 0) and then three letters. Hence

$$22 \cdot 9 \cdot 9 \cdot 9 \cdot 22 \cdot 22 \cdot 22 = 170\,772\,624$$

(In fact there are less than this number because the authorities confine the arrangement of the three letters to certain patterns in order to identify where the vehicle was registered.)

How many new registrations may there be in one year?

$$9 \cdot 9 \cdot 9 \cdot 22 \cdot 22 \cdot 22 = 7\,762\,392$$

This is because in each year the letter preceding the number is unique.

Definition 1.4.2 The product of positive integers from 1 to n is called a *factorial* and denoted $n!$, that is

$$n! = n(n-1)(n-2) \cdots 3 \cdot 2 \cdot 1$$

Also note that $0! = 1$, by definition.

Permutations

A permutation of r elements is an ordered set of r elements. For example, (a, c, b) is a possible permutation of the elements a, b, c. Another separate permutation of the same elements would be (c, a, b). These permutations are different. We wish to develop a formula for counting the possible distinct permutations of r elements from a set of n elements. To be more formal:

Definition 1.4.3 An arrangement of a set of n objects in a given order is a *permutation* of the objects. An arrangement of $r \leqslant n$ of these objects in a given order is a *permutation of n objects taken r at a time.*

Denote the number of possible permutations of n objects taken r at a time by ^nP_r.

The formula for ^nP_r is given by the theorem below.

Theorem 1.4.1

$$^nP_r = \frac{n!}{(n-r)!}$$

This follows since the first element of an r permutation can be chosen in n ways; following this the second element can be chosen in $n-1$ ways and so on. The rth (last) element in the r permutation can be chosen in $n - (r - 1) = n - r + 1$ ways. Hence

$$^nP_r = n(n-1)(n-2) \cdots (n-r+1)$$
$$= \frac{n(n-1)(n-2) \cdots (n-r+1)(n-r)!}{(n-r)!}$$
$$= \frac{n!}{(n-r)!}$$

Example 1.4.2 How many permutations of two letters from a, b, c are there?

$$^3P_2 = \frac{3!}{1!} = 6$$

The six permutations are $(a, b), (a, c), (b, c), (b, a), (c, a), (c, b)$.

Theorem 1.4.2 The number of permutations of n objects of which n_1 are alike, n_2 are alike, $\ldots, n_r$ are alike is

$$\frac{n!}{n_1! n_2! \cdots n_r!}$$

The logic of this result can best be seen by considering the following example.

Example 1.4.3 How many different arrangement of five letters can be formed using the letters from the word DADDY?

Let us begin by labelling the Ds as D_1, D_2 and D_3. Treating each letter as distinct there are 5! permutations. However, in practice $D_1AD_2D_3Y$ is indistinguishable from $D_3AD_1D_2Y$. The number of distinct permutations is therefore divided by the number of ways the Ds can be ordered. There are 3! of the Ds. Since there is only one A and one Y the number of arrangements is given by

$$\frac{5!}{3!\,1!\,1!} = \frac{120}{6} = 20$$

Combinations

A combination of r elements is an unordered set of r elements. Therefore the combination $\{a, c\}$ is the same as $\{c, a\}$ since the order in which the elements are reported is immaterial. In this sense a combination is just a set in that it is a list of items in no specific order.

It is common in probability and statistics that we wish to know the total possible number of combinations of a given number of objects from a wider set. Therefore we may ask the question: given n objects how many *different groups* of r objects could be formed? Being more formal:

Definition 1.4.4 A *combination* of n objects taken r at a time is any subset of r elements. Denote the number of combinations of n objects taken r at a time by

$$^nC_r \text{ or } \binom{n}{r}$$

In other words an r combination is any selection of r from n where the order does not count.

Theorem 1.4.3

$$^nC_r = \binom{n}{r} = \frac{n!}{(n-r)!\,r!}$$

PROOF Since each combination of n objects taken r at a time determines $r!$ permutations,

$$^nP_r = r!\,^nC_r$$

$$\Rightarrow \quad ^nC_r = \frac{^nP_r}{r!}$$

$$= \frac{n!}{(n-r)!\,r!}$$

Example 1.4.4 How many combinations of two letters from a, b, c are there?

$$^3C_2 = \frac{3!}{1!\,2!} = 3$$

More specifically the three combinations are $\{a, b\}, \{b, c\}, \{a, c\}$.

There is an interesting relationship between the possible combinations of r objects from n and the possible permutations of r objects from n. This is seen from the proof of Theorem 1.4.3 in that

$$^nP_r = {}^nC_r{}^rP_r$$

A good way of understanding this relationship is in the form of tree diagrams. The tree diagram in Fig. 1.10 represents the possible permutations and combinations of two letters from $\{a, b, c\}$. (In this diagram and elsewhere in this text { } brackets are used to denote combinations, since these are sets. In contrast ( ) brackets are used to denote the elements of permutations since these are specific orderings of elements.)

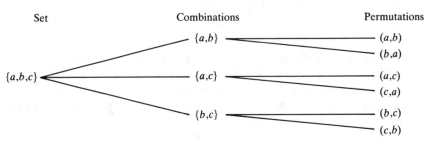

Figure 1.10

Moving from left to right in Fig. 1.10 we can see that a set of three letters produces three combinations of two elements each. Each of these combinations produces two permutations of the same two elements. Therefore in accordance with our results from Examples 1.4.2 and 1.4.4 there are six permutations of two from three and three combinations of two from three. This provides an example of the relationship described above, that is

$$^3P_2 = {}^2C_2{}^2P_2$$

Another example of a tree diagram is used in the accompanying software (Program 11) to explain the relationship between permutations and combinations.

Binomial coefficients

The values of ^nC_r or $\binom{n}{r}$ are often referred to as the binomial coefficients. This is so because of their prominence in the binomial theorem. The binomial theorem gives a general expression for the expansion of $(x + y)^n$.

Theorem 1.4.4 *Binomial theorem*:

$$(x + y)^n = \sum_{k=0}^{n} \binom{n}{k} x^k y^{n-k}$$

Example 1.4.5 Expand the expression $(x + y)^3$:

$$(x + y)^3 = \binom{3}{0} x^0 y^3 + \binom{3}{1} x^1 y^2 + \binom{3}{2} x^2 y^1 + \binom{3}{3} x^3 y^0$$

$$= y^3 + 3xy^2 + 3x^2 y + x^3$$

Notice the numbers in this form of expansion follow Pascal's triangle. This triangle of numbers is given below:

etc.

Notice in Pascal's triangle that every number can be obtained by adding the two numbers diagonally above it: for example 6 is obtained by adding 3 and 3 above it. Each number inside the triangle (i.e. not the lines of 1's on the outside) is derived in the same way. This property is equivalent to the following theorem.

Theorem 1.4.5

$$\binom{n+1}{r} = \binom{n}{r-1} + \binom{n}{r}$$

Multinomial coefficients

The problem of *multinomial coefficients* is to find the coefficients of expressions of x in expansions of the form $(x_1 + x_2 + \cdots + x_r)^n$. This expansion is directly related to the following problem:

A set of n different items is to be divided into r separate groups of respective sizes $n_1, n_2, \ldots, n_r$, where

$$\sum_{i=1}^{n} n_i = n$$

How many different divisions are possible? The answer is

$$\binom{n}{n_1, n_2, \ldots, n_r} = \frac{n!}{n_1! \, n_2! \cdots n_r!}$$

Example 1.4.6

$$\binom{7}{2,3,2} = \frac{7!}{2! \, 3! \, 2!} = 210$$

Example 1.4.7 How many distinct 10 letter sequences can be made with the letters from the word

STATISTICS?

Since there are three Ss, three Ts, two Is, one A and one C, the answer is

$$\binom{10}{3,3,2,1,1} = \frac{10!}{3! \, 3! \, 2! \, 1! \, 1!} = 50\,400$$

Such numbers are the *multinomial coefficients*. The following theorem which generalizes the binomial theorem uses multinomial coefficients to determine the expansion of $(x_1 + x_2 + \cdots + x_r)^n$.

Theorem 1.4.6

$$(x_1 + x_2 + \cdots + x_r)^n = \sum_{n_1 + n_2 + \ldots n_r = n} \binom{n}{n_1, n_2, \ldots, n_r} x_1^{n_1} x_2^{n_2} \cdots x_r^{n_r}$$

Exercises 1.4

Exercise 1.4.1 Evaluate:
  (a) $^4P_2$ (b) $^{10}P_3$ (c) $^8P_2$ (d) $^7P_5$

Exercise 1.4.2 Evaluate:
  (a) $^8C_3$ (b) $^7C_5$ (c) $^4C_4$ (d) $^5C_2$

Exercise 1.4.3 In Scrabble each player chooses seven tiles with letters written on them. How many ways are there of choosing seven letters so that they are all different. How many five letter combinations are there if all five letters are different?

Exercise 1.4.4 (a) Find the number of four letter arrangements that can be formed from the word FRENCH.
  (b) How many of them contain only consonants?

(c) How many contain the letter F?

(d) How many have the vowel as the first letter?

Exercise 1.4.5 There are eight economists and six mathematicians in a room.

(a) How many different committees of three economists and four mathematicians can be formed?

(b) How many different committees of two economists and two mathematicians can be formed?

Exercise 1.4.6 A cricket club consists of 14 players.

(a) How many ways can a team of 11 be selected?

(b) How many ways can the batting order for the team be determined in the club?

(c) In the club there are two players who can keep wicket, four who can bowl and eight other players. How many ways are there of choosing a team consisting of one wicketkeeper and three bowlers?

Exercise 1.4.7 In a game of whist five trumps are dealt to one pair of partners. How many combinations of five trump cards over the two hands are possible?

Exercise 1.4.8 A student has to answer 4 from 10 questions in an examination.

(a) How many choices are there?

(b) How many choices are there if the first two questions are compulsory?

(c) How many choices are there if exactly two of the first five questions must be answered?

(d) How many choices are there if at least two questions from the first five questions must be answered?

Exercise 1.4.9 A level examinations are graded A, B, C, D, E. Assume a candidate passes three A levels.

(a) How many permutations of three different grades are there?

(b) How many combinations of three different grades are there?

(c) How many ways are there of getting two grades the same and a third different?

(d) How many ways are there of getting three A levels of the same grade?

(e) How many possible sets of three A-level results are there?

Exercise 1.4.10 How many eight letter permutations can be formed using the letters from the word HONOLULU?

1.5 AXIOMS OF PROBABILITY

There is considerable controversy regarding the meaning of probability and the interpretation that may be placed on the concept in different circumstances. However, once numerical values have been assigned to the outcomes in an experiment there is complete agreement on the mathematical laws and methodology that govern probability calculations. This section introduces these axioms and laws of probability. Program 8 covers the same material. First we need some definitions.

Definition 1.5.1 The set of all outcomes of a given experiment is called the *sample space* and is denoted by S.

Example 1.5.1 The sample space of tossing two coins is

$$S = \{(H, H), (H, T), (T, H), (T, T)\}$$

Definition 1.5.2 Any subset E of the sample space is known as an *event*. The laws and definitions of set theory outlined in Section 1.3 apply to any collection of events.

Definition 1.5.3 Two events E, F are said to be *mutually exclusive* if

$$E \cap F = 0$$

Definition 1.5.4 If $E_1, E_2, \ldots, E_n$ are events, the union of these events is

$$\bigcup_{i=1}^{n} E_i = E_1 \cup E_2 \cup \cdots \cup E_n$$

Definition 1.5.5 Likewise the intersection of a collection of events is

$$\bigcap_{i=1}^{n} E_i = E_1 \cap E_2 \cap \cdots \cap E_n$$

Definition 1.5.6 De Morgan's laws may accordingly be generalized:

$$\left(\bigcup_{i=1}^{n} E_i \right)' = \bigcap_{i=1}^{n} E_i'$$

$$\left(\bigcap_{i=1}^{n} E_i \right)' = \bigcup_{i=1}^{n} E_i'$$

Definition 1.5.7 *Axioms of probability.* Let S be a sample space, let ξ be the set of events and let P be a real-valued function defined on ξ. Then P is called a *probability function* and $P(E)$ is called the probability of event E if the following axioms hold:

A1. $$0 \leqslant P(E) \leqslant 1$$

The probability of E is a number between 0 and 1.

A2. $$P(S) = 1$$

With probability 1 the outcome will be a point in the sample space.

A3. If $E_1, E_2, \ldots, E_n$ is a sequence of mutually exclusive events then

$$P\left(\bigcup_{i=1}^{\infty} E_i \right) = \sum_{i=1}^{\infty} P(E_i)$$

i.e. for mutually exclusive events the probability of at least one of these events occurring is just the sum of their respective probabilities.

For the simple two-event case then A3 implies that if E and F are mutually exclusive then

$$P(E \cap F) = P(E) + P(F)$$

Theorem 1.5.1 $$P(\varnothing) = 0$$

PROOF If E is any event then, by A3,

$$P(E) = P(E \cup \varnothing) = P(E) + P(\varnothing)$$

Subtracting $P(E)$ from both sides gives the result.

Theorem 1.5.2 $$P(E') = 1 - P(E)$$

PROOF Since $S = E \cup E'$

By A2:

$$1 = P(S) = P(E \cup E')$$

By A3:

$$P(E \cup E') = P(E) + P(E')$$

Therefore,

$$P(E') = 1 - P(E)$$

Theorem 1.5.3 If $E \subset F$, then $P(E) \leqslant P(F)$.

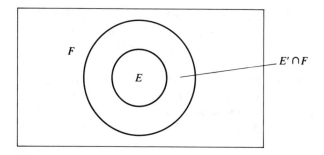

Figure 1.11

PROOF Since $E \subset F$ then

$$F = E \cup (E' \cap F)$$

The Venn diagram in Fig. 1.11 illustrates this.

Since E and $(E' \cap F)$ are mutually exclusive then, by A3,

$$P(F) = P(E) + P(E' \cap F)$$

Theorem 1.5.4 $P(E \cup F) = P(E) + P(F) - P(E \cap F)$

PROOF $E \cup F$ can be written as two mutually exclusive events. Write
$P(E \cup F) = P(E \cup [E' \cap F])$ (See Fig. 1.12).

By A3:

$$P(E \cup F) = P(E) + P(E' \cap F)$$

But

$$P(E' \cap F) = P(F) - P(E \cap F)$$

Hence

$$P(E \cup F) = P(E) + P(F) - P(E \cap F)$$

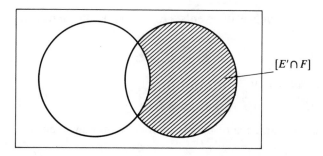

Figure 1.12

Corollary 1.5.1
$$P(E \cup F \cup G) = P(E) + P(F) + P(G) - P(E \cap F)$$
$$- P(E \cap G) - P(F \cap G)$$
$$+ P(E \cap F \cap G)$$

Definition 1.5.8 *Finite probability space.* Let S be a finite sample space, say $S = \{e_1, e_2, \ldots, e_n\}$. A *finite probability space* is obtained by assigning to each point $e_i \in S$ a real number p_i, called a probability of e_i, satisfying the following properties:

(*a*) $p_i \geq 0$

(*b*) $\displaystyle\sum_{i=1}^{n} p_i = 1$

Definition 1.5.9 For many experiments it is natural to assume that all outcomes in the sample space are equally likely to occur. Such a finite probability space is an *equiprobable* or *uniform space*. If such a space S contains n points then the probability of each is the same:

$$P\{1\} = P\{2\} = P\{n\}$$

$$\Rightarrow \quad P\{i\} = \frac{1}{n}$$

Further, if any event E contains r points then its probability is r/n, that is

$$P(E) = \frac{\text{number of elements in } E}{\text{number of elements in } S}$$

Example 1.5.2 Consider a pack of 52 cards. Let

$$A = \{\text{card is a spade}\}$$
$$B = \{\text{card is a picture}\}$$

$$P(A) = \frac{13}{52} = \frac{1}{4} \qquad P(B) = \frac{12}{52} = \frac{3}{13} \qquad P(A \cap B) = \frac{3}{52}$$

Definition 1.5.10 A sequence of events $\{E_n, n \geq 1\}$ is an *increasing sequence* if

$$E_1 \subset E_2 \subset \cdots \subset E_n \subset E_{n+1} \subset \cdots$$

and a *decreasing sequence* if

$$E_1 \supset E_2 \supset \cdots \supset E_n \supset E_{n+1} \supset \cdots$$

If E_n is an increasing sequence of events then define a new event

$$\lim_{n \to \infty} E_n = \bigcup_{i=1}^{\infty} E_i$$

If E_n is a decreasing sequence of events then define a new event

$$\lim_{n\to\infty} E_n = \bigcap_{i=1}^{\infty} E_i$$

Theorem 1.5.5 If $\{E_n, n \geq 1\}$ is either an increasing or decreasing sequence of events then

$$\lim_{n\to\infty} P(E_n) = P(\lim_{n\to\infty} E_n)$$

PROOF The proof of this proposition is beyond the scope of this text but a proof can be found in Ross (1984, pp. 44–45).

Exercises 1.5

Exercise 1.5.1 List all possible outcomes if a coin is tossed four times. What probabilities should be assigned to the points of the sample space corresponding to the experiment?

Exercise 1.5.2 A box contains two black balls and one white ball. Two balls are to be drawn from this box with replacement. Construct two sample spaces for this experiment. What probabilities would you assign to the points of the two sample spaces constructed?

Exercise 1.5.3 An urn contains 16 balls, of which six are red, seven are white and three are blue. If four balls are taken at random and without replacement, find the probability that: (*a*) each of the four balls is red; (*b*) none of the four balls is red; (*c*) there is at least one ball of each colour.

Exercise 1.5.4 Compute the probability of being dealt at random and without replacement a 13-card bridge hand consisting of: (*a*) six hearts and seven spades; (*b*) six spades, one heart, two diamonds and four clubs: (*c*) 13 cards of the same suit; (*d*) 13 clubs.

Exercise 1.5.5 An urn contains eight balls. Three of the balls are red and five are black. Three balls are to be drawn successively at random and without replacement. (*a*) Compute the probability that the colours alternate. (*b*) Compute the probability that the first black ball is chosen from the urn on the third draw.

Exercise 1.5.6 Three groups of children contain respectively two girls and two boys, two girls and one boy and one girl and three boys. A child is selected at random from each (giving a sample of three children).

(*a*) Give a sample space for the sex composition of the three children chosen in this experiment and assign probabilities to each of its elements.

(b) Let E_1 be the event 'at least two boys in the sample' and E_2 the event 'all the children in the sample are the same sex'. Find the probability of either E_1 or E_2 occurring and explain why this probability is not equal to the sum of the probability of E_1 and the probability of E_2.

Exercise 1.5.7 Let A and B be events in a sample space S, such that

$$P(A) = 0.4 \qquad P(B) = 0.3 \qquad P(A \cap B) = 0.1$$

Find the probabilities of:

(a) $A \cup B$ (b) B' (c) A' (d) $A' \cap B$ (e) $A' \cup B'$ (f) $A \cup B'$

Exercise 1.5.8 A fair die is rolled twice. Calculate the probability of getting (a) a total of 4, (b) a total of less than 4, (c) a total that is an even number.

Exercise 1.5.9 A box contains four coins, three of which are honest coins but the fourth of which has heads on both sides. If a coin is selected at random from the box and then is tossed two times, what is the probability that two heads will be obtained?

1.6 CONDITIONAL PROBABILITY AND INDEPENDENCE

Often it is of interest to calculate probabilities when some partial information concerning the result of the experiment is available. For example, we may wish to know the probability that it will rain tomorrow given that the weather forecast is 'overcast'. In such a situation the desired probabilities are *conditional* ones. This section discusses the concept of conditional probability in some detail. The same material is also presented in Program 9.

We shall now study the way in which the probability of an event F changes after it has been learned that some other event E has occurred.

Definition 1.6.1 Let E and F be two events in S with $P(E)$, $P(F) > 0$. Denote by $P(F|E)$ the probability of F given that E has occurred. The *conditional probability* of F given E is

$$P(F|E) = \frac{P(E \cap F)}{P(E)}$$

One way of thinking of this notion is to consider oneself standing somewhere inside the area of the circle E (Fig. 1.13) and ask the question: what is the probability that one is also in circle F?

The answer must be that it depends on how big the area $E \cap F$ is

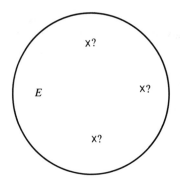

Figure 1.13

compared to E. (This is assuming that probability is proportional to area.)

Consider the two examples in Fig. 1.14. In the right-hand diagram the likelihood of being in F given that one is already in E is much higher than in the left-hand Venn diagram. The reason is that the area of intersection $E \cap F$ is proportionately larger in the right-hand diagram, i.e. the size of $P(F|E)$ depends on the size of $P(E \cap F)$ relative to $P(E)$.

One could also consider the act of conditioning as reducing the sample space from S to only E (in this case) and asking how big the portion of F is in E. Thus, computing $P(F|E)$ is essentially finding $P(F)$ with respect to E rather than with respect to the original sample space S.

Hence a logical definition is

$$P(F|E) = \frac{P(E \cap F)}{P(E)}$$

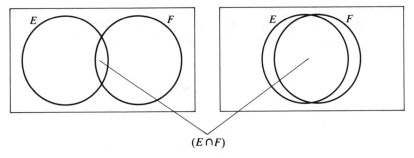

$(E \cap F)$

Figure 1.14

Theorem 1.6.1 Let S be a finite equiprobable space with events A and E. Then

$$P(A|E) = \frac{\text{number of elements in } (A \cap E)}{\text{number of elements in } E}$$

Example 1.6.1 Toss a fair coin twice. What is the conditional probability that both tosses result in heads, given that the first toss does?

$$\text{Let } F = \{(H, H)\}$$
$$E = \{(H, H), (H, T)\}$$
$$P(F|E) = \frac{P(E \cap F)}{P(E)}$$
$$= \frac{\frac{1}{4}}{\frac{2}{4}} = \frac{1}{2}$$

One problem with the use of Venn diagrams in the illustration of probability concepts is that the areas represented in the diagrams are not always proportional to the probabilities associated with them. This can sometimes be confusing. Consider an alternative diagram to represent conditional probability that does not have this drawback. The approach is best illustrated with the use of an example.

Example 1.6.2 Consider that there are two events A and B with probabilities $P(A) = .5$; $P(B) = .4$ and $P(A \cap B) = .2$. This may be represented in the usual way in the Venn diagram in Fig. 1.15.

An alternative presentation which will aid an understanding of conditional probability is given in Fig. 1.16. In this figure the various probabilities are directly represented by the areas of the four adjacent rectangles. [This diagram is used by Meyer (1970) to describe an example of conditional probability.]

The shaded area represents the event B. The left shaded rectangle is the event $A \cap B$ and the right shaded rectangle the event $A' \cap B$. Likewise the other two rectangles represent event $A \cap B'$ (upper left) and $A' \cap B'$ (upper right).

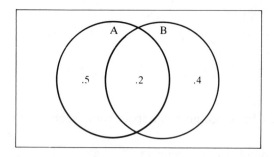

Figure 1.15

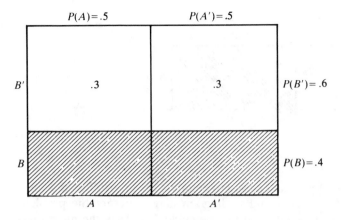

Figure 1.16

Now suppose we wish to compute $P(B|A)$. This can be determined from the areas in Fig. 1.16. More specifically the proportion of B in A is .4. This can be checked by the formula

$$P(B|A) = \frac{P(A \cap B)}{P(A)} = \frac{.2}{.5} = .4$$

Therefore the conditional probability may be represented by Fig. 1.17. Note that if A has occurred all the probability is associated with A, that is $P(A) = 1$, and none with A', that is $P(A') = 0$. Note that the individual probabilities in A have changed but the relative proportions remain the same, that is 2:3.

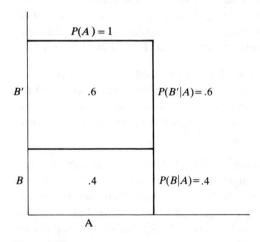

Figure 1.17

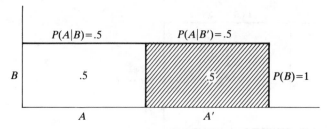

Figure 1.18

The analogous logic can be used to compute the probability of A given B, that is $P(A|B)$. Also a similar diagram may represent the problem. Therefore consider now being inside the circle B and ask the question of what is the probability of being in A or in A'. The relevant diagram is Fig. 1.18.

Note in this diagram that the sample space under consideration is B, that is $P(B) = 1$ (the shaded area on the right). Now, given that B has occurred what is the probability of A or A'? Since equal probability is attached to each then the answer is $P(A|B) = .5$ and $P(A'|B) = .5$. The result may be verified:

$$P(A|B) = \frac{P(A \cap B)}{P(B)} = \frac{.2}{.4} = .5 \qquad P(A'|B) = \frac{P(A' \cap B)}{P(B)} = \frac{.2}{.4} = .5$$

Exercises 1.6

Exercise 1.6.1 Bowl I contains six red balls and four blue balls and bowl II is empty. Five of the 10 balls in bowl I are selected at random and without replacement and put in bowl II. One ball is then drawn at random from bowl II. Given that this ball is blue, find the conditional probability that two red balls and three blue balls are transferred from bowl I to bowl II.

Exercise 1.6.2 A bridge club has 14 members (seven married couples). Four members are randomly chosen to form the club committee. Find the probability that (*a*) the committee consists of two men and two women; (*b*) the members of the committee are all of the same sex; (*c*) the committee contains no married couple.

Exercise 1.6.3 If the number shown on a single throw of a die is 5 or 6, two balls are drawn with replacement from a bag A; otherwise two balls are drawn with replacement from bag B. Bag A contains four green balls and one yellow ball while B contains two green and one yellow ball. Find the probability that one green ball will be drawn. Make explicit the role played by conditional probability.

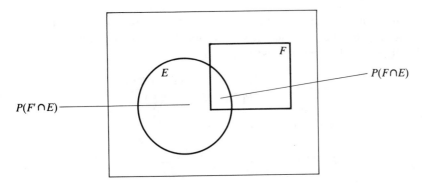

Figure 1.19

Bayes' theorem

Conditional probabilities are not only important as new probabilities given some additional information but may also be used in computing unconditional probabilities. From the definition of conditional probability we may rearrange this expression to produce the following useful formula:

Theorem 1.6.2 $P(E \cap F) = P(E|F)P(F)$

PROOF Obvious from Definition 1.4.3.

Notice also that $P(E)$ can be written as

$$P(E) = P(E \cap F) \cup P(F' \cap E)$$

The Venn diagram in Fig. 1.19 illustrates this result.

Also, since $(F \cap E)$ and $(F' \cap E)$ are mutually exclusive then

$$P(E) = P(F \cap E) + P(F' \cap E)$$

However, substituting from our definition of conditional probability above we can write

$$P(E) = P(E|F)P(F) + P(E|F')P(F')$$

This equation simply says that the probability of the event E is a weighted average of the conditional probability of E given that F has occurred and the conditional probability of E given that F has not occurred. Each conditional probability is given as much weight as the event that it is conditioned on. This formula is useful as it is often easier to ascertain the probability of an event by first conditioning on whether some second event has occurred.

This formula is also useful in the statement of Bayes' theorem when considering the special case of two events. Using our definition of conditional probability we may write

$$P(F|E) = \frac{P(E \cap F)}{P(E)} = \frac{P(E|F)P(F)}{P(E)}$$

Using our formula for $P(E)$ we may write

$$P(F|E) = \frac{P(E|F)P(F)}{P(E|F)P(F) + P(E|F')P(F')}$$

This result is a version of Bayes' theorem in the case of two events. The result and its usefulness may best be illustrated by example. This result is also derived in Program 10.

Example 1.6.3 Alison and Claire wash up 60 and 40 per cent of the time respectively. While washing up Alison breaks a dish with a probability of .1 and Claire with a probability of .2. Given that on a particular evening a dish is broken, what is the probability that Alison is to blame or Claire is to blame?

$P(A) = .6$ denotes the probability that Alison washes up
$P(C) = .4$ denotes the probability that Claire washes up
$P(B|A) = .1$ is the conditional probability that a dish is broken given that A is washing up
$P(B|C) = .2$ is the conditional probability that a dish is broken given that C is washing up
$P(B) = P(B|A)P(A) + P(B|C)P(C)$
$\qquad = .1(.6) + .2(.4)$
$\qquad = .14$

Using Bayes' theorem:

$$P(C|B) = \frac{P(B|C)P(C)}{P(B)} \qquad P(A|B) = \frac{P(B|A)P(A)}{P(B)}$$
$$\qquad = .2(.4)/.14 \qquad\qquad\qquad = .1(.6)/.14$$
$$\qquad = 4/7 \qquad\qquad\qquad\qquad = 3/7$$

Example 1.6.4 In Copland the probability of being arrested (event A) in an average day if you are black (event B) is $P(A|B) = .005$ and if you are white (event W) is $P(A|W) = .0001$. The community is made up of 75 per cent whites and 25 per cent blacks. What is the probability that if an arrest is made the person involved is black?

$$P(B|A) = \frac{P(A \cap B)}{P(A)} = \frac{P(A|B)P(B)}{P(A|B)P(B) + P(A|W)P(W)}$$

$$= \frac{.005(.25)}{.005(.25) + .0001(.75)}$$

$$= .943$$

The analogous result to Theorem 1.6.2 for the intersection of any number of events can be expressed in Corollary 1.6.1. This result is needed for the proof of Bayes' theorem.

Corollary 1.6.1 *Multiplication theorem.* For any events $F_1, F_2, \ldots, F_n$,

$$P(F_1 \cap F_2 \cap \cdots \cap F_n) = P(F_1)P(F_2|F_1)P(F_3|F_1 \cap F_2) \cdots$$
$$P(F_n|F_1 \cap F_2 \cap \cdots \cap F_n)$$

Having introduced Bayes' theorem in the two-event context it is appropriate to elaborate. The analogous result with a large number of possible events is important and we shall derive it formally.

Theorem 1.6.3 *Bayes' theorem.* Let $F_1, F_2, \ldots, F_n$ form a partition of a sample space S, i.e. these events are mutually exclusive with $P(F_i) > 0$ and

$$\bigcup_{i=1}^{n} F_i = S$$

Let E be any other event with $P(E) > 0$.
Then for $j = 1, \ldots, n$,

$$P(F_j|E) = \frac{P(E|F_j)P(F_j)}{\sum_{i=1}^{n} P(E|F_i)P(F_i)}$$

This situation is represented in the Venn diagram in Fig. 1.20 for the case where $n = 4$. Notice that F_1, F_2, F_3, F_4 are a complete partition of the sample space S in that they are mutually exclusive but together they account for the whole sample space. Event E, where $P(E) > 0$, is also drawn in this diagram in such a way that it overlaps with some of the F_i.

PROOF We know that $E = S \cap E$. Then since the set S is made up from the F_i mutually exclusive events then

$$E = (F_1 \cup F_2 \cup \cdots \cup F_n) \cap E$$

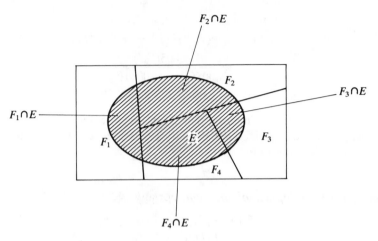

Figure 1.20

Multiplying out (using the distributive law) gives

$$E = (F_1 \cap E) \cup (F_2 \cap E) \cup \cdots \cup (F_n \cap E)$$

Since $(F_i \cap E)$ are mutually exclusive then

$$P(E) = P(F_1 \cap E) + P(F_2 \cap E) + \cdots + P(F_n \cap E)$$

By Theorem 1.6.2,

$$P(E) = P(F_1)P(E|F_1) + P(F_2)P(E|F_2) + \cdots + P(F_n)P(E|F_n) \qquad (*)$$

Also, for any j from Definition 1.6.1,

$$P(F_j|E) = \frac{P(F_j \cap E)}{P(E)}$$

Substituting $(*)$ into the denominator and Theorem 1.6.2 into the numerator gives

$$P(F_j|E) = \frac{P(E|F_j)P(F_j)}{\sum_{i=1}^{n} P(E|F_i)P(F_i)}$$

This result is Bayes' theorem.

The result can be seen from the 'tree diagram' in Fig. 1.21. Given that one of the paths to E has been followed, what is the probability that a particular F_j was used to reach it? The answer is that this probability is expressed as the probability of following F_j and E divided by the total probability associated with all the possible paths leading to E. For example, if $j = 2$ the probability of the path in bold provides us with the $P(F_2 \cap E)$ or $P(E|F_2)P(F_2)$. When expressed relative to the weighted sum of the path probabilities leading to E, that is $\sum P(E|F_i)P(F_i)$, this gives us $P(F_2|E)$.

If we consider the events F_i as being 'possible hypotheses' about the truth of some proposition then Bayes' theorem may be interpreted as

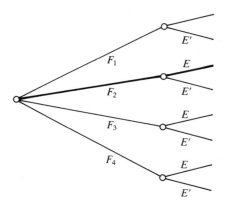

Figure 1.21

showing how these preconceived probabilities $[P(F_i)]$ about these hypotheses before the experiment should be modified by the evidence of the experiment. These notions have some more precise terminology associated with them.

Definition 1.6.2 Usually the probabilities of the events known beforehand, i.e. the $P(F_i)$, are called *prior probabilities*. Likewise, the conditional probabilities deduced from prior probabilities and other known conditional probabilities are referred to as *posterior probabilities*.

Two examples of the use of Bayes' theorem in the context of more than two events may help to clarify this important theorem and the concepts involved.

Example 1.6.5 Let A_i be the event that an item was produced by machine i ($i = 1, 2, 3$) and let B be the event that the selected item is defective.

Assume that the probability of an item selected at random being produced by i is

$$P(A_1) = .2 \qquad P(A_2) = .3 \qquad P(A_3) = .5$$

Also let the probability $P(B|A_i)$ that an item produced by i is defective be

$$P(B|A_1) = 0.01 \qquad P(B|A_2) = 0.02 \qquad P(B|A_3) = 0.03$$

What is $P(A_2|B)$?

$$P(A_2|B) = \frac{P(A_2)P(B|A_2)}{\Sigma_{i=1}^{3}P(A_i)P(B|A_i)}$$

$$= \frac{(0.3)(0.02)}{(0.2)(0.01) + (0.3)(0.02) + (0.5)(0.03)}$$

$$= 0.26$$

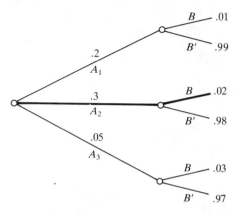

Figure 1.22

This position can be illustrated using a 'tree diagram' where the path $P(A_2|B)$ is drawn in bold (Fig. 1.22). The path has probability $P(A_2 \cap B) = .3 \times .02$. This must be considered relative to the probability of taking any path leading to B.

Example 1.6.6 You meet someone who has had an operation for a 'lump'. The prior probabilities that for any given patient this lump is a simple inflammation is $P(I) = .65$, a benign tumour is $P(B) = .30$, a malignant tumour is $P(M) = .05$. The probability that an operation (O) is required for each ailment is $P(O|I) = .001$, $P(O|B) = .15$, $P(O|M) = .8$. What, therefore, are the posterior probabilities that the person you met had a simple inflammation, a benign tumour or a malignant tumour?

$$P(I|O) = \frac{P(I)P(O|I)}{P(O)}$$

$$= \frac{P(I)P(O|I)}{P(I)P(O|I) + P(B)P(O|B) + P(M)P(O|M)}$$

$$= \frac{.0065}{.0065 + .045 + .04} = .07$$

$$P(B|O) = \frac{P(B)P(O|B)}{P(O)}$$

$$= \frac{P(B)P(O|B)}{P(I)P(O|I) + P(B)P(O|B) + P(M)P(O|M)}$$

$$= \frac{.045}{.0065 + .045 + .04} = .49$$

$$P(M|O) = \frac{P(M)P(O|M)}{P(O)}$$

$$= \frac{P(M)P(O|M)}{P(I)P(O|I) + P(B)P(O|B) + P(M)P(O|M)}$$

$$= \frac{.04}{.0065 + .045 + .04} = .44$$

Therefore, although malignant lumps are far more likely to need an operation, when we weight this by the low probability of a malignant tumour it turns out that it is more likely that the person we met had a benign tumour.

Exercises 1.6 (*continued*)

Exercise 1.6.4 Two coins are placed in a bag. Assume that one coin has both faces as tails and that the other is a normal coin. One coin is selected at random from the bag and tossed. It lands on the ground and you are allowed to see only the upward face of the coin, which is tails. What is the probability that the hidden face is also tails?

Exercise 1.6.5 A certain disease is present in about 1 out of 1000 persons in a given population, and a programme of testing is to be carried out using a detection device that gives a positive reading with probability .99 for a diseased person and with probability .05 for a healthy person. What is the probability that a person who has a positive reading actually has the disease?

Exercise 1.6.6 Two balls are drawn at random without replacement from an urn containing w white balls and b black balls. What is the probability that the second ball drawn will be white?

Exercise 1.6.7 Three widget machines A, B and C produce respectively 60, 25 and 15 per cent of the total widget output of a factory. The percentages of defective output of these machines are respectively 1, 3 and 2 per cent. A widget is selected at random and is found defective. Find the probability that the item was produced by machine C.

Exercise 1.6.8 At the Makepeace Methodist College, 4 per cent of the men and 1 per cent of the women are taller than 2 metres. Only 30 per cent of the students are women. If a student is selected at random and is taller than 2 metres, what is the probability that the student is a woman?

Exercise 1.6.9 The sample space for an experiment consists of the four mutually exclusive joint events $(H_1$ and $E)$, $(H_1$ and $E')$, $(H_2$ and $E)$ and

(H_2 and E') formed from the events H_1, H_2, E and E'. Explain how the Bayes theorem can be used to modify the prior probabilities of H_1 and H_2 if E is observed. Explain what happens to this procedure if (*a*) E and H_1 are mutually exclusive and (*b*) E and H_1 are independent.

Exercise 1.6.10 A doctor has devised a test to determine whether or not a patient needs a certain operation. The test is positive 80 per cent of the time when an operation is needed and 40 per cent of the time when an operation is not needed. The test is given to patients for whom the doctor has a prior probability of 0.5 that they need the operation. What is the posterior probability that an operation is required? If the patient is given two tests what is the posterior probability that an operation is needed if both tests are positive?

Exercise 1.6.11 The General Election is only 6 months away. A by-election has been called in the constituency of Redland. The PM is resigned to the fact that the Tories will lose the byelection, but thinks their chances of winning the impending General Election depend greatly on the share of the vote that the Tories can secure in Redland. The Tories calculate that their chances of winning the General Election are:

0.9 if the Tories secure greater then 35 per cent of the Redland votes
0.5 if the Tories secure between 25 and 35 per cent of the Redland votes
0.1 if the Tories secure less than 25 per cent of the Redland votes

They estimate that they have 0.1 chance of getting at least 35 per cent of the Redland votes and 0.8 chance of getting between 25 and 35 per cent of the Redland vote.

The Tories were beaten in the General Election. Based on the information above, what is the probability that they achieved less than 25 per cent of the Redland votes?

Exercise 1.6.12 Sunderland Football Club are in deep relegation trouble (again). Their chances of remaining in the Second Division depend to a large extent on a crucial match with another lowly rated team (Lowly United) in the second to last match of the season. A Sunderland supporter assigns the following probabilities to remaining in the Second Division:

0.9 if they beat Lowly United
0.2 if they lose to Lowly United
0.6 if they draw with Lowly United

The supporter assesses the probabilities of the Lowly game as:

Winning : 0.4
Drawing : 0.5
Losing : 0.1

At the end of the season Sunderland are relegated. Based on the above information, what is the probability that they beat Lowly in that second to last game of the season?

Independence

The concept of independence is central in probability theory.

Definition 1.6.3 Two events E and F are said to be *independent* if

$$P(E \cap F) = P(E)P(F)$$

More formally, the occurrence of E is not affected by whether F has occurred.

An example of two independent events may be the events of Cambridge winning the next Oxford–Cambridge boat race and England winning the next World Cup. These events would be independent since the occurrence of one cannot materially affect the possibility of the other occurring.

Proposition 1.6.1 If E and F are independent then

$$P(E|F) = P(E)$$

PROOF Follows from Definition 1.6.1.

Example 1.6.7 The notion of independence can be illustrated with our numerical Example 1.6.2. In this example $P(A) = .5$, $P(B) = .4$ and $P(A \cap B) = .2$.

Since A and B are independent if

$$P(A \cap B) = P(A)P(B)$$

then from our example we can see that

$$P(A \cap B) = .2 \quad \text{and} \quad P(A)P(B) = (.4)(.5) = .2$$

Hence A and B are independent.

Also recall that two events are independent if $P(A|B) = P(A)$ and $P(B|A) = P(B)$. Since $P(A) = .5$ and we computed $P(A|B) = .5$ earlier, then A and B are independent.

Likewise we also know that $P(B) = .4$ and we computed $P(B|A) = .4$.

Therefore in this example we have been using we know that A and B are independent events since the occurrence of B does not affect the probability of A and vice versa.

One further crucial point to note is that independent events cannot be mutually exclusive.

Proposition 1.6.2 If E and F are independent then so are E and F'.

PROOF It is always true that

$$P(E \cap F') = P(E) - P(E \cap F)$$

Since E and F are independent,

$$P(E \cap F) = P(E)P(F)$$
$$\begin{aligned} P(E \cap F') &= P(E) - P(E)P(F) \\ &= P(E)[1 - P(F)] \\ &= P(E)P(F') \end{aligned}$$

Example 1.6.8 Given a pack of cards let the event that a selected card is an ace be E and that it is a spade be F. Hence

$$P(E) = 1/13 \qquad P(F) = 1/4 \qquad P(E \cap F) = 1/52$$

Hence these events are independent.

Definition 1.6.4 Two events that are not independent are said to be *dependent*.

An example of dependent events could be the event Cambridge winning the next boat race and the event Oxford winning the next boat race. These events are obviously dependent since the occurrence of one precludes the occurrence of the other. (Setting the possibility of a dead heat aside.)

Definition 1.6.5 Three events E, F and G are independent if

$$P(E \cap F \cap G) = P(E)P(F)P(G) \qquad P(E \cap F) = P(E)P(F)$$
$$P(E \cap G) = P(E)P(G) \qquad P(F \cap G) = P(F)P(G)$$

Sometimes in studying the concept of independence there is a tendency to become confused with the concept of mutually exclusive events. It is important to be clear about the following relationships:

1. Mutually exclusive events with non-zero probabilities are dependent. To see this consider A and B to be mutually exclusive with non-zero probabilities; thus,

$$P(A \cap B) = 0 \qquad P(A) \neq 0 \qquad P(B) \neq 0$$

If these events were independent, then we know that

$$P(A \cap B) = P(A)P(B)$$

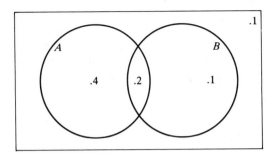

Figure 1.23

However, to satisfy mutual exclusivity the left-hand side must be zero. Correspondingly, we know that the right-hand side must be positive since both $P(A)$ and $P(B)$ are non-zero. Therefore there is a contradiction and mutually exclusive events must be dependent. For example, if Oxford and Cambridge both have a positive probability of winning the boat race then the two events cannot be independent. These two events are mutually exclusive and the probability of one event occurring has a direct implication for the probability of the other occurring.

2. Dependent events are not necessarily mutually exclusive. The example below of non-empty, intersecting sets that are dependent is sufficient to demonstrate this proposition.

   Example 1.6.9 $P(A) = .6$, $P(B) = .3$, $P(A \cap B) = .2$ (Fig. 1.23).

   $$P(A|B) = P(A \cap B)/P(B) = .2/.3 \neq P(A)$$

   Hence A and B are dependent.

3. Independent events are not necessarily mutually exclusive. The example below of non-empty, intersecting sets that are independent is sufficient to demonstrate this proposition.

   Example 1.6.10 $P(A) = .6$, $P(B) = .3$, $P(A \cap B) = .1$ (Fig. 1.24).

   $$P(A|B) = P(A \cap B)/P(B) = .1/.2 = .5 = P(A)$$
   $$P(B|A) = P(A \cap B)/P(A) = .1/.5 = .2 = P(B)$$
   $$\text{or } P(A \cap B) = P(A)P(B) = .5(.2) = .1$$

   Hence A and B are independent.

Exercises 1.6 (*continued*)

Exercise 1.6.13 Decide whether the following events are independent:

(*a*) Sunderland FC being relegated from their division of the football league and Portsmouth FC being promoted

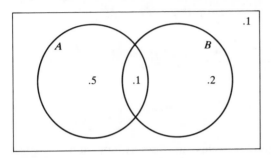

Figure 1.24

(*b*) It raining tomorrow and it raining the day after tomorrow

(*c*) Winning the Pools and winning on the Premium Bonds

(*d*) A meteor landing on the Eiffel Tower and the Eiffel Tower falling down in the next 50 years.

(*e*) An English woman winning the 100 metres in the next Olympics and Blackpool being the venue of the Labour Party conference in the year 2050.

Having reached this point in the exposition it is appropriate for the reader to begin to use Program 12. This program may be used to help with the exercises that follow.

Exercises 1.6 (*continued*)

Exercise 1.6.14 Consider tossing three dice. Is the probability of getting a combined total score of at least 10 independent of getting a 6 on the first die?

Hint: Using Program 12 let $A = 6$, $B = 6$, $C = 6$, $X: A + B + C > 10$ and $Y: A = 6$.

Exercise 1.6.15 Consider flipping four coins. Is the probability of obtaining two heads and two tails independent of obtaining four heads?

Exercise 1.6.16 Consider tossing two dice and flipping two coins. Is the probability of getting two heads and a score of 5 on the dice independent?

Exercise 1.6.17 In Exercise 1.6.16 above, if a head is worth 1 and a tail is worth 2 and each side of the die is worth its face value, what is the probability of getting a score of at least 10? Is this probability independent of getting two tails on the two coins?

CHAPTER TWO

DISCRETE RANDOM VARIABLES
AND DISTRIBUTIONS

2.1 INTRODUCTION

The outcomes of many experiments can be summarized by the counting of numerical values and therefore involves discrete variables. A discrete random variable occurs when the values taken by this type of numerical outcome is uncertain. For example, many board games use the outcome of throwing two dice to govern play. Often we may be interested in counting the sum of two dice. Such an outcome would therefore be a number between 2 and 12. The precise number that will occur on any throw of the dice (or performance of the experiment) cannot be predicted with certainty before throwing. Therefore such a number is called a *random variable*.

The concept of a random variable is fundamental to probability theory and statistics. Random variables can be divided into three types: discrete, continuous and mixed. In this chapter we first consider discrete random variables and their distribution.

2.2 DISCRETE RANDOM VARIABLES

Often when an experiment is performed we are concerned about some function of the outcome (a *random variable*) as opposed to the actual outcome itself. It is possible to assign probabilities to the possible values of the random variable.

Example 2.2.1 Consider random variable X to be the number of heads in a sequence, s, of 10 tosses of a coin. Then it is possible to assign a number $X(s)$ for any sequence, for example HHHTTHTTTH $\Rightarrow X(s) = 5$.

Example 2.2.2 Consider selecting a person at random from some population and recording the number of people in his or her immediate family. This number will be a discrete random variable.

A random variable may be more formally defined:

Definition 2.2.1 A *random variable* (r.v.) X on a sample space S is a function that assigns to each element $s \in S$ one and only one real number $X(s) = x$. The *range* of X is the set of real numbers $\mathbb{R}$.
  [*Note*: The notation to be used is capital letters (for example X) for random variables and lower case letters (for example x) for their possible values.]

The concept of a random variable can be represented as in Fig. 2.1, where $X(.)$, the random variable, is mapping elements in the sample space to points on the real line. (This diagram is also described in Program 13.)
  In what follows it is necessary to make a clear distinction between two types of random variable (r.v.): *discrete* and *continuous*. Discrete random

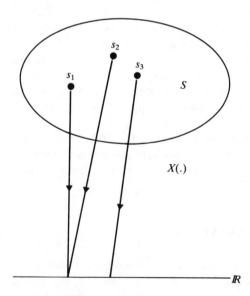

Figure 2.1

Table 2.1

d_2	d_1					
	1	2	3	4	5	6
1	(1,1)	(1,2)	(1,3)	(1,4)	(1,5)	(1,6)
2	(2,1)	(2,2)	(2,3)	(2,4)	(2,5)	(2,6)
3	(3,1)	(3,2)	(3,3)	(3,4)	(3,5)	(3,6)
4	(4,1)	(4,2)	(4,3)	(4,4)	(4,5)	(4,6)
5	(5,1)	(5,2)	(5,3)	(5,4)	(5,5)	(5,6)
6	(6,1)	(6,2)	(6,3)	(6,4)	(6,5)	(6,6)

variables are defined on discrete sample spaces and their range is finite (or countable). Continuous random variables are defined over continuous intervals and their range is uncountable.

To make the concepts introduced seem less abstract consider again our example of throwing two dice. In this case the sample space is the whole set of points in our lattice in Fig. 1.8. Writing this out the possible sample points are as shown in Table 2.1, where the first number, d_2, in each pair denotes the number on the first die and the second number in the pair, d_1, denotes the number on the second die.

If we now consider our random variable, X, to be the sum of the numbers on the two dice, then the function

$$X = d_1 + d_2$$

determines our random variable.

Therefore the value of X can easily be computed for each sample point. The matrix corresponding to the sample space above is given in Table 2.2.

Table 2.2

d_2	d_1					
	1	2	3	4	5	6
1	2	3	4	5	6	7
2	3	4	5	6	7	8
3	4	5	6	7	8	9
4	5	6	7	8	9	10
5	6	7	8	9	10	11
6	7	8	9	10	11	12

2.3 PROBABILITY FUNCTIONS AND CUMULATIVE DISTRIBUTION FUNCTIONS

The value that a discrete random variable takes is determined by the outcome of an experiment. Associated with each possible value that a discrete random variable can take is a well-defined probability.

Consider again our example of throwing two dice. (This problem is also examined in Program 14.) We defined one example of a random variable X to be

$$X = d_1 + d_2$$

The possible values that X may take are $2, 3, 4, \ldots, 12$. However, these numerical values are not equally likely. If each of the possible 36 outcomes in Table 2.2 is equally likely, then $X = 2$ can only occur when $d_1 = 1$ and $d_2 = 1$; however, $X = 3$ can occur if $d_1 = 1$ and $d_2 = 2$ *or* if $d_1 = 2$ and $d_2 = 1$. Correspondingly, $X = 4$ can occur in three ways: $d_1 = 1$ and $d_2 = 3$, or $d_1 = 3$ and $d_2 = 1$, or $d_1 = 2$ and $d_2 = 2$. Likewise, there are six possible ways in which an outcome of 7 could occur.

Let us summarize this information in terms of possible values of X and the associated likelihood of each value occurring. These values of X and their associated probabilities can be written out in the form of a table which constitutes a *probability function*, $f(x)$, in which $f(x)$ records the probability that $X = x$ for each value of x. (This concept will be more formally defined after considering this example.)

x	$f(x)$
2	1/36
3	2/36
4	3/36
5	4/36
6	5/36
7	6/36
8	5/36
9	4/36
10	3/36
11	2/36
12	1/36

This function is sometimes more loosely called a probability distribution. (This terminology can sometimes be confused with the concept of a cumulative distribution function and so the reader should be wary of this.)

This information can also be presented in the form of a 'bar chart', as

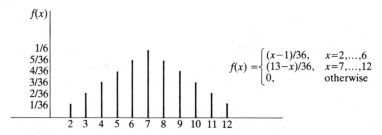

Figure 2.2

in Fig. 2.2. In this diagram the height of each bar at each value of x represents the probability of that value occurring.

Using such a probability function it is easy to calculate various probabilities. For example, if we wish to know the probability of throwing a sum greater than 9,

$$f(x > 9) = f(10) + f(11) + f(12)$$
$$= 3/36 + 2/36 + 1/36$$
$$= 1/6$$

Likewise, the probability of throwing an even sum is

$$f(X = 2, 4, 6, 8, 10, 12) = f(2) + f(4) + f(6) + f(8) + f(10) + f(12)$$
$$= 1/36 + 3/36 + 5/36 + 5/36 + 3/36 + 1/36$$
$$= 1/2$$

Having introduced an example we are now able to define a probability function more formally.

Definition 2.3.1 If X is a discrete random variable, the function given by $f(x) = P(X = x)$ for each x within the range of X is called the *probability function* (p.f.).

(*Note*: The same concept is variously called: a probability distribution, probability density function, probability mass function.).

From the postulates of probability theory it follows that:

Theorem 2.3.1 A function is a probability function of a discrete random variable X iff
(a) $f(x) \geqslant 0$, for each value of $x \in \mathbb{R}$.
(b) $\Sigma_x f(x) = 1$, where the summation operates over the values of $x \in \mathbb{R}$.

The proof of these results is beyond the scope of this text. We can simply treat (a) and (b) above as properties. Property (a) simply requires that $f(x)$ is never negative. The second property requires that the probabilities associated with a given random variable sums to unity. This is a constraint on the probability we wish to describe, which ensures that the random variable is logically consistent.

A probability function is not the only way in which a random variable can be represented. A second important concept is a cumulative distribution function. Such a function also completely describes how probability is assigned to values of a random variable.

There are many problems in which it is of interest to know the probability that the value of the random variable is less than or equal to some real number b.

For example, suppose we want to compute the probability of throwing a sum of 5 or less than 5 with two dice. This can, of course, be calculated by using the probability function

$$P(X \leqslant 5) = f(1) + f(2) + f(3) + f(4) + f(5)$$
$$= 5/12$$

However, we may want to express the probability that x is less than a specific value of b for all possible values of x. Therefore, we require a function that tells us the probability that X is less than or equal to x for *each* possible value of x that the random variable may take. Such a function is called a *cumulative distribution function* and is denoted by $F(x)$.

The cumulative distribution function for the sum of the two-dice example is:

x	$F(x)$
$x < 2$	0
$x \leqslant 2$	1/36
$x \leqslant 3$	3/36
$x \leqslant 4$	6/36
$x \leqslant 5$	10/36
$x \leqslant 6$	15/36
$x \leqslant 7$	21/36
$x \leqslant 8$	26/36
$x \leqslant 9$	30/36
$x \leqslant 10$	33/36
$x \leqslant 11$	35/36
$x \leqslant 12$	1

Notice that each successive value of $F(x)$ is obtained by adding all previously occurring values to the next largest value of $f(x)$, that is

$$F(x \leqslant 2) = f(2)$$
$$F(x \leqslant 3) = f(2) + f(3)$$
$$F(x \leqslant 4) = f(2) + f(3) + f(4)$$
$$\vdots \qquad \vdots$$
$$F(x \leqslant 12) = f(2) + \ldots + f(12)$$

Hence the name 'cumulative' distribution function. It is necessary to define this concept more formally and discuss its properties.

Definition 2.3.2 If X is a discrete random variable the function given by

$$F(b) = P\{X \leqslant b\} = \sum_{x \leqslant b} f(x)$$

(where $-\infty < b < \infty$) is called the *cumulative distribution function*, c.d.f., of X.

Theorem 2.3.2 Some properties of the cumulative distribution function F are:

(a) F is a non-decreasing function; i.e. if $a < b$ then $F(a) \leqslant F(b)$. The cumulative distribution function cannot have a negative slope.

(b) $\lim_{b \to \infty} F(b) = 1$. The limiting value of the cumulative distribution function is 1 as the random variable becomes arbitrarily large.

(c) $\lim_{b \to -\infty} F(b) = 0$. The limiting value of the cumulative distribution function is 0 as the random variable becomes arbitrarily small.

(d) F is *right continuous*; i.e. for any b and any decreasing sequence b_n, $n \geqslant 1$, that converges to b,

$$\lim_{n \to \infty} F(b_n) = F(b)$$

This means that any step function that represents a cumulative distribution function takes the upper value at the steps in the function, i.e. in the example in Fig. 2.3b the value at the steps is denoted by the small circle.

PROOF

(a) If $a < b$ then the event $\{X \leqslant a\}$ must be contained in the event $\{X \leqslant b\}$ and so cannot have a larger probability.

(b), (c) and (d) all follow from the continuity property of probabilities, i.e. Theorem 1.5.5, and as a result are beyond the scope of this book.

Having explored the concepts of a random variable, a probability function and a cumulative distribution function it is worth reflecting that these are theoretical concepts that may not occur in practical examples. For example, the observed distributions of scores of dice tossed in a given number of trials do not always conform to the theoretical probability functions we have examined. This point is best considered in some detail by simulating the tossing of dice. This can be done using Program 17. This program allows you to compare the simulated distribution of the total score generated by tossing a given number of dice a specified number of times, with the theoretical distribution that probability theory predicts would come about. This program helps us to appreciate the conditions under which empirical distributions converge to theoretical distributions.

Example 2.3.1 Consider the random variable X to be the number of heads that appear on two tosses of a fair coin. This example is also described in Program 13. The probability function for this example is drawn in Fig. 2.3a, and written analytically as follows:

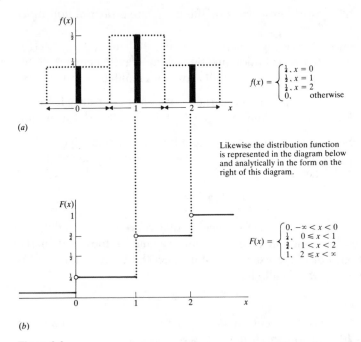

$$f(x) = \begin{cases} \frac{1}{4}, & x = 0 \\ \frac{1}{2}, & x = 1 \\ \frac{1}{4}, & x = 2 \\ 0, & \text{otherwise} \end{cases}$$

(a)

Likewise the distribution function is represented in the diagram below and analytically in the form on the right of this diagram.

$$F(x) = \begin{cases} 0, & -\infty < x < 0 \\ \frac{1}{4}, & 0 \leq x < 1 \\ \frac{3}{4}, & 1 < x < 2 \\ 1, & 2 \leq x < \infty \end{cases}$$

(b)

Figure 2.3

Various points should be noted about these functions and their representation:

1. Figure 2.3a is a *bar chart* and represents the probability associated with each discrete value of x. The sum of ordinates in a bar chart are one, i.e. the sum of the lengths of the 'bars' in Fig. 2.3a is one. Sometimes probability functions are represented by a *histogram*. In Fig. 2.3a such a histogram is shown by the dotted outline. The area

under a histogram sums to one. Such a representation involves putting a 'continuous' interpretation on the random variable. This is indicated by the implicit representation of the relative probability of values between 0 and 1 and 1 and 2 using the dotted lines in Fig. 2.3a. Such a histogram representation for a discrete random variable taking only integer values may therefore be misleading.

2. The distribution function in Fig. 2.3b has discontinuous jumps at $x = 0, 1, 2$ of $\frac{1}{4}$, $\frac{1}{2}$ and $\frac{1}{4}$ which are the ordinates in Fig. 2.3a. Therefore it is possible to obtain the probability function from the distribution function.

3. The value of the cumulative distribution function, $F(x)$, at any value of n is obtained from the higher step; thus the value at 1 is $\frac{3}{4}$ not $\frac{1}{4}$. This is expressed by describing the distribution function to be *right continuous*.

4. For any $x_2 > x_1$ then $F(x_1) \geqslant F(x_2)$, i.e. the cumulative distribution function is *monotonically increasing*.

Exercises 2.3

Exercise 2.3.1 Let $f(x) = x/10$, $x = 1, 2, 3, 4$, zero elsewhere, be the probability function of X. Find the distribution function, $F(x)$, and sketch its graph. Evaluate $P(X = 1 \text{ or } X = 2)$, $P(1 \leqslant X \leqslant 3)$, $P(X = 1 \text{ or } X = 4)$, $P(X \leqslant 3)$, $P(3 \leqslant X \leqslant 10)$.

Exercise 2.3.2 Let $f(x) = 1/3$, $x = -1, 0, 1$, zero elsewhere, be the probability function of X. Find the distribution function, $F(x)$, and sketch its graph. Evaluate $P(|X| = 1)$, $P(0 \leqslant X \leqslant 4)$, $P(X = 0)$, $P(-\frac{1}{2} \leqslant X \leqslant \frac{1}{2})$.

Exercise 2.3.3 A-level examination passes are graded A, B, C, D and E. University selectors attach 5 points for an A, 4 points for a B, 3 points for a C, 2 for a D and 1 for an E. Assume a candidates passes three A levels but has equal probability of any of the five grades in each examination. What is the probability function of the total score, X, on three A levels?

(*Hint*: Use your answer to Exercise 1.4.9.)

Evaluate (*a*) $P(X = 6)$, (*b*) $P(X = 7, 8)$, (*c*) $P(11 \leqslant X \leqslant 14)$, (*d*) $P(X \leqslant 5)$, (*e*) $P(0 \leqslant X \leqslant 3)$. (*f*) What is the probability of getting the same grade on all three A levels?

Exercise 2.3.4 Let the random variable Y be the largest score on a pair of fair dice when they are tossed. Find the probability function, $f(y)$. Evaluate (*a*) $P(Y \leqslant 3)$, (*b*) $P(4 < Y \leqslant 6)$, (*c*) $P(-\frac{3}{2} \leqslant Y \leqslant \frac{3}{2})$, (*d*) $P(Y \text{ is even})$, (*e*) $P(Y = 5)$.

Exercise 2.3.5 In bridge 'high' cards are often valued in a points score. An ace is worth 4 points, a King 3 points, a Queen 2 points and a Jack 1 point. You know your partner has two high cards; construct the probability function on the total point score in her hand. What is the probability that your partner has (*a*) more than 5 points, (*b*) 3 points or less, (*c*) exactly 4 points? What is the probability that your partner is holding two high cards with the same point value?

Exercise 2.3.6 Let $f(x) = (x^2 + 1)/c$, $x = -3, -2, -1, 0, 1, 2, 3$, zero elsewhere be the probability function of a random variable X. Find the value of c. Sketch the distribution function, $F(x)$. Evaluate $P(X \leq 1)$ and $P(\frac{7}{8} < X \leq 3)$.

Exercise 2.3.7 (*a*) Are the following valid probability functions?
 (i) $f(x) = 1 - 2x$, $x = 0, \frac{1}{4}, \frac{3}{4}$
 (ii) $f(x) = x/19$, $x = 1, 2, 3, 4, 5, 6$
 (iii) $f(x) = cx$, $x = 2, 4, 6, 8$
 (iv) $f(x) = (\frac{1}{2})^x$, $x = 1, 2, 3, 4, \ldots$
 (v) $f(x) = \frac{1}{2}$, $x = 1, 3$
 (*b*) Are the following functions valid cumulative distribution functions?
 (i) $F(x) = x/3$, $x = -1, 0, 1, 2, 3$
 (ii) $F(x) = x + \frac{1}{2}$, $x = 0, \frac{1}{8}, \frac{1}{4}, \frac{1}{2}$
 (iii) $F(x) = (|x| + 1)/2|x|$, $x = -2, -\frac{3}{2}, -1$
 (iv) $F(x) = |x|/4$, $x = -1, 0, 1, 2, 3, 4$
 (v) $F(x) = \frac{1}{4}$, $x = -1, 0, 1, 2, 3$
 (vi) $F(x) = 1 - 1/x$, $x = 2, 3, 4, \ldots$

Exercise 2.3.8 Let Z be a random variable with the cumulative distribution function:

Z	1	3	5	7	9
F(z)	0	$\frac{1}{8}$	$\frac{3}{8}$	$\frac{5}{8}$	1

Find the probability function. Evaluate (*a*) $P(Z \leq 7)$, (*b*) $F(7) - F(5)$, (*c*) $P(Z = 9)$, (*d*) $P(-1 \leq Z \leq \frac{3}{2})$.

2.4 SPECIAL DISCRETE DISTRIBUTIONS

A probability distribution can be thought of as the theoretical analogue of an empirical frequency distribution, and any function satisfying the definition can be used as a distribution function. In practice, specific forms of probability distributions are used. This section introduces two of these special probability distributions. These distributions are related to each other in various ways. We describe some of these relationships here.

The distributions dealt with in this chapter are the *binomial* and *Poisson* which are discrete distributions and can conveniently handle certain kinds of processes involving counting. In the next chapter three distributions that are continuous are introduced. These are associated with random variables taking values within an interval on the real line.

These distributions are selected for special treatment for several reasons. The first is that some concreteness is lent to ideas discussed in previous chapters. Second, these particular distributions are widely used by practising statisticians and knowledge of them is part of basic statistical literacy. Furthermore, some of their properties are not true of all distributions. Knowledge of the relationships between these distributions is also useful and helps to deepen our understanding of the processes that underlie the theory. Finally, the standard distributions discussed here arise naturally in the context of certain real-life or physical processes. The binomial distribution, for instance, is concerned with the number of 'successes' that occur in a sequence of experiments, the outcome of each of which is one of only two alternatives: 'success' or 'failure'. The model can be applied to a wide variety of situations in product testing, bioassay, quality control and other areas. The Poisson distribution can be used in the analysis of spatial and temporal occurrence of 'rare' events.

Because some of the properties of these special distributions are subtle and difficult to grasp without some sort of illustration, we have used the computer programs to illustrate the distributions and their properties. The treatment of the distributions on the computer screen is less formal than the treatment given in this chapter. Programs 19 to 22 deal with binomial and Poisson distributions while Program 28 shows the Poisson as an approximation to the binomial.

2.5 BERNOULLI TRIALS AND THE BINOMIAL DISTRIBUTION

The material in this section refers to Programs 19 and 20. Before introducing our first special distribution we need to define two important concepts: the *Bernoulli trial* and a *sequence of Bernoulli trials*.

A Bernoulli trial is an experiment that has only two possible outcomes. The two outcomes are often referred to as 'success' and 'failure', although these names are not always appropriate and may sometimes be confusing.

Definition 2.5.1 A random variable has a *Bernoulli distribution* if its probability function is given by

$$p(0) = P\{X = 0\} = 1 - p$$
$$p(1) = P\{X = 1\} = p$$

where $0 \leq p \leq 1$ is the probability that a trial is a success.

Example 2.5.1 Sex of children. The sex of an unborn child is a Bernoulli trial with possible outcomes 'male' and 'female'.

Example 2.5.2 Quality control. A single item of output from a production process may be defective or not. Production of such an item can be viewed as a Bernoulli trial with possible outcomes 'satisfactory' and 'unsatisfactory'.

Example 2.5.3 Job search. An applicant for a job may either get an offer ('success') or be rejected ('failure').

Notice that the definition of a Bernoulli trial does not specify probabilities or restrict them in any way. In particular, there is no requirement that the probabilities of 'success' and 'failure' be equal. We denote the probability of 'success' by the letter p. This probability has, of course, some value between zero and one. Because there are only two possible outcomes, it must be true that the probability of 'failure' is equal to $1 - p$.

Considering the examples again we might expect that in Example 2.5.1 the value of p assigned to 'male' is about .5. In Example 2.5.2, a probability of 'satisfactory' as low as .5 would most likely be unacceptable to the production manager, whereas the probability of a job-seeker receiving an acceptable offer will depend on his skills and ability, among other things. We now turn to our second definition.

Definition 2.5.2 A *sequence of Bernoulli trials* is a set of independent Bernoulli trials, each with the same probability of 'success'.

The two special features of this definition that need to be highlighted are the requirements of independence and identical probabilities. In a production process, a breakdown of part of the equipment may change the probability that the 'satisfactory' outcome occurs. Thus even though a quality controller may be taking independent random samples from the flow of output, it is not necessarily the case that his sampling will fit the model described in the definition above if the breakdown occurs in mid-sample. In fact, one can think of a quality controller's task as that of determining whether a violation of the constant probability condition has occurred.

As an example of a violation of the independence assumption, consider again the job search example. If the second employer that the job-seeker approaches knows that the job-seeker has been previously rejected and if his hiring decision is influenced (one way or the other) by this knowledge, then the two Bernoulli trials will not constitute a sequence, because the probability of success in the second trial will be influenced by the outcome of the first.

We are now in a position to describe the first of our special distributions. It is called the *binomial distribution*. Suppose we have a sequence of Bernoulli trials of fixed length n. The number of 'successes' in such a sequence can be anything from zero to n. The count of 'successes' constitutes a random variable and the binomial distribution is simply its distribution.

The binomial distribution is important because it is a natural model for use in many experimental and sampling contexts.

Example 2.5.4 Testing a new drug for side effects. Ten laboratory rats are each given the same dose of a new headache medicine, and tested for side effects. This can be modelled as ten Bernoulli trials with outcomes 'side effects' or 'no side effects'. The number of rats that suffer no side effects is a random variable, with possible values $0, 1, \ldots, 10$. If the assumptions of independence and equal probability apply, this random variable has a binomial distribution.

Example 2.5.5 Market research. A market researcher is investigating car-buying behaviour. He interviews 20 households (chosen at random) and asks if they have bought a car in the previous 12 months. This can be modelled as a sequence of 20 Bernoulli trials with outcomes 'bought' or 'did not buy'. The number of cars purchased is a random variable that has possible values $0, \ldots, 20$. If the probability of a car purchase is the same for each household, this random variable has a binomial distribution.

We learned earlier that a probability distribution consists of two elements: a list of possible values of a random variable and a list of the probabilities to be assigned to them. We are now in a position to construct the binomial probability distribution. The possible values of a random variable with the binomial distribution are easily determined. Since the number of 'successes' must be a non-negative integer and can be no greater than the number of trials in the sequence, the set of possible values must be $\{0, 1, \ldots, n\}$.

The probabilities associated with these possible values are a little more difficult to determine. Suppose that we are interested in calculating the probability of k 'successes' and that the probability of 'success' in each Bernoulli trial is p. The trials are independent and therefore the probability of k 'successes' followed by $n - k$ 'failures' is $p^k(1 - p)^{n-k}$. This is not, however, the probability that we seek, because we have assumed in this calculation a specific order for the k 'successes' and $n - k$ 'failures'. The probability of any other ordering is also $p^k(1 - p)^{n-k}$; consequently the probability of k 'successes' and $n - k$ 'failures' with unspecified order is just $p^k(1 - p)^{n-k}$ multiplied by the number of possible orders. As we saw above in Chapter 1 the number of ways of ordering k objects among n is $\binom{n}{k}$. Therefore the required probability is $\binom{n}{k}p^k(1 - p)^{n-k}$.

We can write this conclusion more formally.

Definition 2.5.3 A random variable X has a *binomial* distribution with parameters (n, p) when it represents the number of successes that occur in n independent Bernoulli trials each with probability p of success. For short, we will sometimes write 'X is $b(n, p)$'.

Its probability function is

$$b(n, p) = p(k) = \binom{n}{k}p^k(1 - p)^{n-k} \qquad i = 0, 1, \ldots, n$$

The $\binom{n}{k}$ term refers to the number of ways of ordering k successes in n trials. The $p^k(1 - p)^{n-k}$ term is the probability of observing k successes and $n - k$ failures in a given order.

Example 2.5.6 To illustrate the use of Definition 2.5.3 consider tossing four coins. What is the probability function of the number of heads? Let X be the number of heads. The four tosses form a sequence of Bernoulli trials each with probability $\frac{1}{2}$. Therefore X is $b(4, \frac{1}{2})$ (see Fig. 2.4):

$$P\{X = 0\} = \binom{4}{0}\left(\tfrac{1}{2}\right)^0\left(\tfrac{1}{2}\right)^4 = \tfrac{1}{16}$$
$$P\{X = 1\} = \binom{4}{1}\left(\tfrac{1}{2}\right)^1\left(\tfrac{1}{2}\right)^3 = \tfrac{4}{16}$$
$$P\{X = 2\} = \binom{4}{2}\left(\tfrac{1}{2}\right)^2\left(\tfrac{1}{2}\right)^2 = \tfrac{6}{16}$$
$$P\{X = 3\} = \binom{4}{3}\left(\tfrac{1}{2}\right)^3\left(\tfrac{1}{2}\right)^1 = \tfrac{4}{16}$$
$$P\{X = 4\} = \binom{4}{4}\left(\tfrac{1}{2}\right)^4\left(\tfrac{1}{2}\right)^0 = \tfrac{1}{16}$$

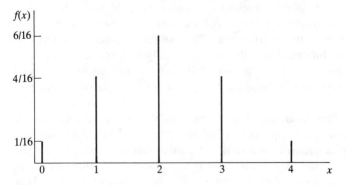

Figure 2.4

Example 2.5.7 Suppose we have a sequence of four Bernoulli trials with probability of 'success', $p = \frac{1}{4}$. The distribution of the number of 'successes' is

k	$P(X = k)$
0	$\binom{4}{0}\left(\frac{1}{4}\right)^0\left(\frac{3}{4}\right)^4 = 1 \times 1 \times \frac{81}{256} = \frac{81}{256}$
1	$\binom{4}{1}\left(\frac{1}{4}\right)^1\left(\frac{3}{4}\right)^3 = 4 \times \frac{1}{4} \times \frac{27}{64} = \frac{108}{256}$
2	$\binom{4}{2}\left(\frac{1}{4}\right)^2\left(\frac{3}{4}\right)^2 = 6 \times \frac{1}{16} \times \frac{9}{16} = \frac{54}{256}$
3	$\binom{4}{3}\left(\frac{1}{4}\right)^3\left(\frac{3}{4}\right)^1 = 4 \times \frac{1}{64} \times \frac{3}{4} = \frac{12}{256}$
4	$\binom{4}{4}\left(\frac{1}{4}\right)^4\left(\frac{3}{4}\right)^0 = 1 \times \frac{1}{256} \times 1 = \frac{1}{256}$

Other examples are given in the computer program accompanying this section (Program 19).

Before leaving the subject of the binomial distribution one further interesting property may be described. It is most clearly stated in the form of a theorem.

Theorem 2.5.1 If X is $b(n,p)$, where $0 < p < 1$, then as k goes from 0 to n, $P\{X = k\}$ first increases monotonically then decreases monotonically, reaching its largest value when k is the largest integer less than or equal to $(n + 1)p$.

PROOF A formal proof is beyond the scope of this text but an example of this result is contained in Example 2.5.6. Here $(n + 1)p = (4 + 1)\frac{1}{2}$ $= 2\frac{1}{2} \Rightarrow k = 2$, which is confirmed by the probability function of X (see Fig. 2.4).

Exercises 2.5

Exercise 2.5.1 Demonstrate the following two facts about a random variable X which has the binomial distribution with parameters n and p:

(a) $n - X$ has a binomial distribution with parameters n and $1 - p$.

(b) X is symmetrically distributed around a if and only if $p = \frac{1}{2}$ and $a = n/2$.

Exercise 2.5.2 A model aeroplane has 10 possible modes of failure. Assuming that the modes are independent and that the probability of any one of them occurring is 0.2, compute the probability that at least two modes of failure have occurred given that one has occurred.

2.6 THE POISSON DISTRIBUTION

The material in this section refers to Programs 21 and 22.

The second distribution that we consider is also concerned with counting. The Poisson distribution gives the probability of a given number of occurrences of a 'rare' event within a given time period or spatial interval. We have seen that the binomial distribution deals with the count of 'successes' in a sequence of Bernoulli trials, when the number of experiments is known and finite. One way of thinking of the Poisson distribution is as a limiting case of the binomial distribution, where the number of experiments is very large and the probability of 'success' quite small. In this sense a success is a rare event.

We will use this fact to develop the distribution later. First some examples.

> **Example 2.6.1** Radioactive particles arriving at a Geiger counter. The arrival of a radioactive particle at a Geiger counter is a rare event that occurs at various points of time. What is the probability of $0, 1, 2, \ldots$ arrivals in a given minute? The answer is given by the Poisson distribution.

> **Example 2.6.2** V-1 attacks on London. What is the probability of $0, 1, 2, \ldots$ V-1 hits on a given block in London? Assuming that blocks are of constant size the answer is given by the Poisson distribution. (For an alternative non-probabilistic explanation see Thomas Pynchon: 'Gravity's Rainbow'.)

> **Example 2.6.3** Injuries by horse kicks in the Prussian army. This is a celebrated example of a random variable whose observed distribution is apparently described well by the Poisson distribution. The probability of any one man being kicked and injured is quite low. What is the probability of $0, 1, 2, \ldots$ injuries in any given regiment?

We use the Geiger counter example to continue the argument. Suppose that each minute is divided into 60 seconds and that the probability of more than one particle arriving within each second is zero. Then we could model our problem as a sequence of 60 Bernoulli trials with some probability p of success in each trial. The difficulty with this is guaranteeing that the probability of more than one particle arriving within each second is zero.

Is there any way that we can reformulate the problem in order to overcome this difficulty? Suppose we were to subdivide the seconds into 1/60 seconds. Then the probability of more than one arrival within each

1/60 second interval would be closer to zero than the probability of more than one arrival in a single second. Indeed, if we continue to subdivide the interval in this manner, we will eventually solve our difficulty. What we are doing, in effect, is to increase the number of Bernoulli trials, n, and to reduce p (the probability of success) in each trial. Notice, however, that it must be the case that np remains constant. (If the probability of an arrival in a given 1/60 second is p_0, then the probability of an arrival in a given second must be $60p_0$. In the first case $n = 60, p = p_0$. In the second $n = 1$, $p = 60p_0$. In both cases $np = 60p_0$.) The probability of k arrivals in a minute can thus be written as a limit of a binomial probability as n becomes large and np remains constant. Thus we can state a formal result.

Proposition 2.6.1 The distribution of a Binomial random variable tends to a Poisson distribution when n becomes large and p small and np remains constant.

PROOF We need only consider the limit as n approaches infinity and impose the condition that np remains constant:

$$P(X = k) = \lim_{\substack{n \to \infty \\ np = \lambda}} \binom{n}{k} p^k (1-p)^{n-k}$$

where λ is a constant.
Noting that:

$$\lim_{n \to \infty} \left(1 - \frac{\lambda}{n}\right)^n = e^{-\lambda}$$

we can simplify this expression as follows:

$$
\begin{aligned}
P(x = k) &= \lim_{n \to \infty} \frac{n!}{k!(n-k)!} \left(\frac{\lambda}{n}\right)^k \left(1 - \frac{\lambda}{n}\right)^{n-k} \\
&= \lim_{n \to \infty} \frac{\lambda^k}{k!} \left(1 - \frac{\lambda}{n}\right)^n \frac{n(n-1)\cdots(n-k+1)}{n^k} \left(1 - \frac{\lambda}{n}\right)^{-k} \\
&= \frac{\lambda^k}{k!} \lim_{n \to \infty} \left(1 - \frac{\lambda}{n}\right)^n \left(1 - \frac{1}{n}\right)\left(1 - \frac{2}{n}\right)\cdots\left(1 - \frac{k+1}{n}\right)\left(1 - \frac{\lambda}{n}\right)^{-k} \\
&= \frac{\lambda^k}{k!} e^{-\lambda}
\end{aligned}
$$

This expression defines the Poisson distribution.

Definition 2.6.1 A random variable X, taking values $0, 1, 2, \ldots$, is a *Poisson* random variable with parameter λ if for some $\lambda > 0$ it has a probability function:

$$p(k) = P\{X = k\} = e^{-\lambda}\frac{\lambda^k}{k!} \qquad k = 0, 1, 2, \ldots$$

This function is indeed a probability function since

$$\sum_{k=0}^{\infty} p(i) = e^{-\lambda} \sum_{k=0}^{\infty} \frac{\lambda^k}{k!} = e^{-\lambda}e^{\lambda} = 1$$

We could have arrived at the same expression for the V-1 example by taking each block of London and subdividing it into quarters, eighths, etc., until the probability of more than one hit in any given subdivision is zero. In general, this will only occur in the limit as the number of subdivisions approaches infinity. We leave it to the reader to work out the appropriate story for the injured Prussian cavalrymen.

Example 2.6.4 Suppose $\lambda = .5$; then the Poisson distribution is as follows:

k	$P(x = k)$
0	.607
1	.303
2	.076
3	.013
$\vdots$	$\vdots$
etc.	etc.

Example 2.6.5 A phenomenon that is described well by a Poisson probability function is the number of misprints on a page in a book. Let $\lambda = 1/2$. Then the probability of at least one error on a given page would be

$$P\{X \geqslant 1\} = 1 - P\{X = 0\} = 1 - e^{-1/2} \approx .395$$

Example 2.6.6 The Poisson random variable is usually a good approximation to infrequent occurrences over time, e.g. the number of earthquakes during a given time span. Assuming a Poisson process is valid and $\lambda = 2$ in a one-week time interval, find the probability that at least three earthquakes occur in the next two weeks.

$$P\{N(2) \geqslant 3\} = 1 - P\{N(2)=0\} - P\{N(2)=1\} - P\{N(2)=2\}$$

$$= 1 - e^{-4} - 4e^{-4} - \frac{4^2}{2}e^{-4}$$

$$= 1 - 13e^{-4}$$

Finally, it should be clear from the way in which the Poisson distribution has been described that it can be used as an approximation to the binomial probabilities in any case where n is large and p small. This approximation is explored at greater length in Programs 28.1 and 28.2.

Exercises 2.6

Exercise 2.6.1 Show that the sum of two independent Poisson distributed random variables with parameters λ_1 and λ_2 has a Poisson distribution with parameters $\lambda_1 + \lambda_2$.
Hint: Use the binomial theorem.

Exercise 2.6.2 Suppose that the distribution of horse kicks in regiments of the Prussian army is Poisson with parameter λ. Suppose further that probability of death from a horse kick (given that one has been kicked) is p. Show that the distribution of deaths from horse kicks is Poisson with parameter λp.

THREE

CONTINUOUS RANDOM VARIABLES AND THEIR DISTRIBUTIONS

3.1 INTRODUCTION

When the nature of any random events yield results that take values over an interval of the real line then the variable in question is said to be a *continuous random variable*. For example, X would be a continuous random variable if X is the height of any individual, if X was the arrival time of any British Rail train, if X was the distance of an arrow from the centre of an archery target after the arrow has been shot or if X was the length of time taken for an egg to hatch.

In the last chapter we saw that a discrete random variable can take only a countable number of specific values. Often these values are in a subset of the set of integers. In contrast a continuous random variable can be defined over the entire interval of real numbers. Alternatively, a continuous random variable could be defined over some subset interval of the real line. Since a continuous random variable can take an infinite number of possible values then the outcomes of an experiment involving a continuous random variable are uncountable. This means that the techniques for the analysis of continuous random variables must be different to those used for the analysis of discrete random variables. When an unaccountable number of possible values are involved we cannot use the counting techniques of summation that we did in the analysis of discrete random variables. Instead, we have to use integration, the continuous analogue of summation.

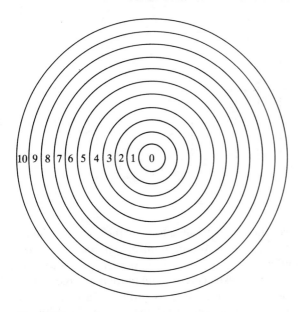

Figure 3.1

3.2 CONTINUOUS RANDOM VARIABLES AND PROBABILITY DENSITY FUNCTIONS

In the last chapter we defined a probability function $f(x) = P(X = x)$ relating probabilities to the possibility of particular discrete value occurrences of a random variable. These values could be portrayed on a histogram. Consider, for example, that the archery target in Fig. 3.1 provides integer scores from 0 to 10 to denote the distance of the flighted arrow from the centre of the target.

This example is also described in two programs: Program 16 describes the example and Program 18 allows the user to choose the conditions of the same simulation.

In firing arrows at the target we could generate a distribution of scores (or distances from the centre of the target.) Such a distribution may take the form of Fig. 3.2 for a moderately experienced archer.

In Fig. 3.2 the integer values represent the grouped value of the distance from the centre of the target in terms of inches. It is of course possible to redefine the rings on this target to make them half their previous width. This may produce the histogram in Fig. 3.3.

Clearly we could repeat this process, continually making the width of the rings smaller and smaller. Being precise about the measurement of the arrows from the centre of the target we could construct a distribution based on the exact measurement of the distance from the bull of all the arrows

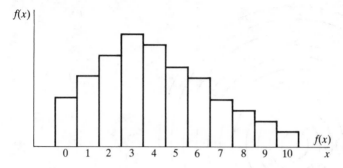

Figure 3.2

fired at the target. In a sense, then, it is possible to view the construction of a continuous probability distribution to be the limit of a process whereby we measure the exact numerical size of the random variable more and more precisely. That is to say, we construct more and more finely measured probability histograms. The limit of this process produces a continuous probability distribution. Such a distribution for our example of the distance of an arrow to a bull is shown in Fig. 3.4.

One consequence of measuring the random variable more and more finely is that the notional probability associated with any specific single value of the random variable is so unlikely as to be indistinguishable from zero. This is because there are an infinite number of values that the random variable can take and hence the occurrence of any specific value is an extremely rare event. Indeed, the property that $P(X = x) = 0$ is a characteristic of a continuous distribution. We shall demonstrate this formally later in this section. Meanwhile an intuitive geometric argument makes the point; with a discrete random variable the probability associated with a

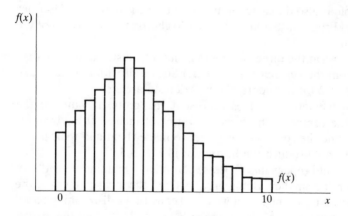

Figure 3.3

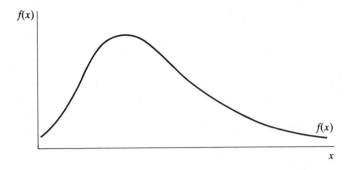

$f(x)$

$f(x)$

x

Figure 3.4

value of the random variable is given by the area of the part of the histogram in question, i.e. a rectangle whose base is centred on the relevant value of X. As the possible number of values X can take increases, the length of the base of the rectangle decreases. As the number of possible values of X approaches infinity then X becomes continuous and the base of the rectangle tends to a point and hence the area of the rectangle tends to zero.

It is necessary to introduce some formal definitions in order to proceed. These definitions and the rest of this section and also Section 3.3 are described in Program 15.

Definition 3.2.1 X is a *continuous* random variable if there is a nonnegative function f, defined for all $x \in (-\infty, \infty)$, having the property that for any set C of real numbers, $C \subset \mathbb{R}$.

$$P\{X \in C\} = \int_C f(x)\,dx$$

The function f is called the *probability density function* (p.d.f.) of X. Less formally this definition states that the probability of X being in the set C can be evaluated by integrating the probability density function over the range of the set C.

The function $f(x)$ provides us with a mathematical method of writing the exact form of the continuous density function and therefore characterizing the distribution of the random variable. Having defined the notion of a continuous random variable and a probability density function it is important to explore further the properties of such a function.

Definition 3.2.2 A function f is a *probability density function* of a continuous random variable X if

(a) $f(x) \geq 0$ for $-\infty < x < \infty$, i.e. the probability density function is greater than or equal to zero over its range.

(b) $P\{X \in (-\infty, \infty)\} = \int_{-\infty}^{\infty} f(x)\,dx = 1$

i.e. the total probability associated with any density is 1.

All probability statements about X can be answered in terms of f. For example, suppose you want to find out the probability that X falls between the values a and b (within the set C) somewhere on the real line. This can be calculated by integrating the relevant density function over the appropriate range.

Let $C = [a, b]$ with $a \leqslant b$; then by Definition 3.2.1,

$$P\{a \leqslant X \leqslant b\} = \int_{a}^{b} f(x)\,dx$$

To find the probability that the random variable X lies between a and b we must integrate the density function between a and b. In terms of Fig. 3.5 this is equivalent to finding the value of the shaded area under the curve representing $f(x)$ between the limits a and b.

Our earlier proposition that the probability associated with any specific value of X is zero can now be seen quite easily. To illustrate this consider our example above and now let $a = b$. This gives

$$P\{X = a\} = \int_{a}^{a} f(x)\,dx = 0$$

Hence the probability that a continuous random variable will assume a given value is zero since the value of an integral of a continuous function at a point is zero.

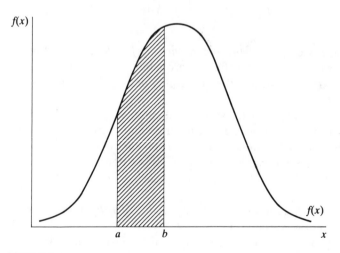

Figure 3.5

3.3 CUMULATIVE DISTRIBUTION FUNCTIONS

As with discrete random variables there are many situations in which one may wish to know the probability that a random variable takes less than or equal to some specific value. For example, the probability that a British Rail train is anything up to 5 minutes late can be found by integrating the relevant density over the appropriate range or evaluating the cumulative distribution function at $x = 5$. Such a cumulative distribution function expresses the probability of $P(X \leq x)$ for any value of x. The more formal definition of a cumulative distribution function is:

Definition 3.3.1 If X is a continuous random variable the function given by

$$F(a) = P\{X \in (-\infty, a)\} = P(X \leq a) = \int_{-\infty}^{a} f(x)\, dx$$

where $f(x)$ is the density function of X at x, is called the *cumulative distribution function* (c.d.f.) of X.

The concept of a cumulative distribution function and its relation with a density function are straightforward to portray in a diagram. Consider Fig. 3.6. In Fig. 3.6a a probability density function, $f(x)$, is drawn. In this diagram the probability that x is less than or equal to a, that is $P(X \leq a)$, is represented by the shaded area to the left of the point under the density function. This probability is calculated by finding the area of the shaded portion under $f(x)$. The same probability can be calculated from the cumulative distribution function. Since $F(a) = P(X \leq a)$, then the probability that X is less than or equal to a is given by the function F and can therefore be read off on the vertical axis in Fig. 3.6b. The importance of the cumulative distribution function, F, is that it will tell us the value of $P(X \leq a)$ for any value of a.

A number of properties of the cumulative distribution function follow almost immediately from its definition:

1. $\lim_{x \to -\infty} F(x) = 0$, that is the probability that the random variable is less than x must approach zero as x gets arbitrarily small.
2. $\lim_{x \to \infty} F(x) = 1$, that is the probability that the random variable is less than x must approach one as x becomes arbitrarily large.
3. $F(a) \leq F(b)$ for $a < b$. Also if a is less b then the cumulative probability associated with b, $F(b)$, must be at least as large as that associated with a, $F(a)$. Therefore a cumulative distribution function can never have a negative slope.
4. If $f(x)$ and $F(x)$ are respectively the probability density function and

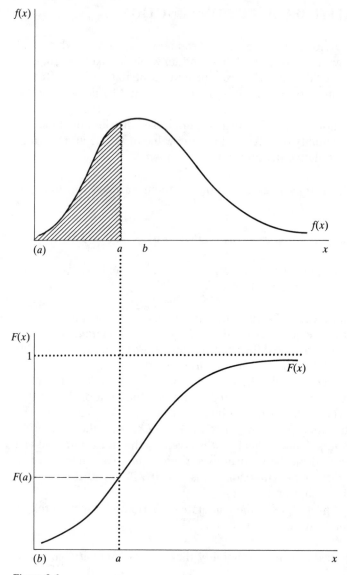

Figure 3.6

cumulative distribution function of a continuous random variable X at x, then

$$P(a \leqslant X \leqslant b) = F(b) - F(a)$$

for any constants a, b where $a \leqslant b$.

5. $F(x)$ is continuous at all points x, $-\infty < x < \infty$, and $\mathrm{d}F(x)/\mathrm{d}x$ exists and is continuous at all points where $f(x)$ is continuous.

6. At all points x where $dF(x)/dx$ exists then

$$f(x) = \frac{dF(x)}{dx}$$

i.e. the probability density function is the derivative of the cumulative distribution function.

Example 3.3.1 X is a continuous random variable with probability density function

$$f(x) = \begin{cases} c(4x - 2x^2) & 0 < x < 2 \\ 0 & \text{otherwise} \end{cases}$$

Find the value of c.
Since

$$\int_{-\infty}^{\infty} f(x)\, dx = 1$$

then

$$c \int_0^2 (4x - 2x^2)\, dx = 1$$

$$c \left[2x^2 - \frac{2x^3}{3} \right]_0^2 = 1$$

$$\Rightarrow \quad c = \tfrac{3}{8}$$

Find $P\{X > 1\}$:

$$P\{X > 1\} = \int_1^{\infty} f(x)\, dx = \tfrac{3}{8} \int_1^2 (4x - 2x^2)\, dx = \tfrac{1}{2}$$

What is the c.d.f. of X?

$$F(x) = \int_{-\infty}^{x} f(x)\, dx = \tfrac{3}{8} \int_0^x (4x - 2x^2)\, dx$$

$$= \tfrac{3}{8} [2x^2 - \tfrac{2}{3}x^3]_0^x$$

$$F(x) = \begin{cases} 0 & x < 0 \\ \tfrac{3}{8}(2x^2 - \tfrac{2}{3}x^3) & 0 \le x < 2 \\ 1 & \text{otherwise} \end{cases}$$

Exercises 3.3

Exercise 3.3.1 The cumulative distribution function for a random variable X is

$$F(x) = \begin{cases} 1 - e^{-2x} & x \ge 0 \\ 0 & x < 0 \end{cases}$$

(a) Find the density function $f(x)$.
(b) Find $P(X > 2)$.
(c) Find $P(-3 < X \leqslant 4)$.

Exercise 3.3.2 Suppose that

$$f(x) = \begin{cases} cxe^{-2x} & x \geqslant 0 \\ 0 & x < 0 \end{cases}$$

is the density function for a random variable X.
(a) Determine c.
(b) Find the cumulative distribution function.
(c) Graph the density and distribution function.
(d) Evaluate $P(X \geqslant 1)$.
(e) Evaluate $P(2 \geqslant X < 3)$.

Exercise 3.3.3 Let Y be a continuous random variable with a density function given by

$$f(y) = \begin{cases} ky^2 & 0 \leqslant y \leqslant 1 \\ 0 & \text{elsewhere} \end{cases}$$

Evaluate k. Find the distribution function, $F(y)$, and graph both $f(y)$ and $F(y)$. Find $P(0 < y < \frac{1}{2})$.

Exercise 3.3.4 The density of a random variable X is given by

$$f(x) = \begin{cases} kx & 0 \leqslant x \leqslant 2 \\ k(4-x) & 2 \leqslant x \leqslant 4 \\ 0 & \text{elsewhere} \end{cases}$$

Evaluate the constant k. Find $P(1 < X < 5)$. Graph the density function and the cumulative distribution function of X.

Exercise 3.3.5 A continuous random variable Y has a probability density function

$$f(y) = \begin{cases} ky^3 & 0 \leqslant y \leqslant 1 \\ 0 & \text{elsewhere} \end{cases}$$

(a) What value does k have to be for f to be a valid density function?
(b) Calculate $P(Y \geqslant 0.5)$.

Exercise 3.3.6 The Cauchy distribution has the density function

$$f(x) = \frac{c}{1+x^2} \qquad -\infty < x < \infty$$

Evaluate c. Find the distribution function $F(x)$ and sketch it. Evaluate $P(0 < x < 1)$. Find the median of this distribution.

Exercise 3.3.7 Given the density function

$$f(x) = \begin{cases} cx(1-x) & 0 < x < 1 \\ 0 & \text{elsewhere} \end{cases}$$

Find c and verify that $F(x)$ is a density function. Evaluate $P(\frac{2}{3} < x < 1)$. Find the distribution function for x.

Exercise 3.3.8 A density function $f(x)$ is defined as follows:

$$f(x) = \begin{cases} kx & \text{for } 0 \leqslant x \leqslant 1 \\ k(2-x) & \text{for } 1 \leqslant x \leqslant 2 \\ 0 & \text{elsewhere} \end{cases}$$

(a) Find k and graph the density function.
(b) Find $P(1 < x < 4)$, $P(0 < x < \frac{3}{2})$, $P(-1 < x < \frac{1}{2})$.
(c) Find the cumulative distribution function and graph it.

Exercise 3.3.9 Let X have the distribution function

$$F(x) = \begin{cases} 0 & x < -1 \\ \dfrac{x+2}{4}, & -1 \leqslant x < 1 \\ 1 & 1 \leqslant x \end{cases}$$

Sketch the graph of $F(x)$ and then compute:
(a) $P(-\frac{1}{2} < X \leqslant \frac{1}{2})$
(b) $P(X = 0)$
(c) $P(X = 1)$
(d) $P(2 < X \leqslant 3)$

Exercise 3.3.10 The density of a continuous random variable X is given by

$$f(x) = \begin{cases} kx(2-x) & 0 \leqslant x \leqslant 2 \\ 0 & \text{otherwise} \end{cases}$$

(a) Find k and graph the density function.
(b) Find $P(1 < x < 2)$, $P(-3 < x < 1)$, $P(-\frac{1}{2} < x < \frac{1}{2})$.
(c) Find the cumulative distribution function and graph it.

3.4 SPECIAL CONTINUOUS DISTRIBUTIONS

In the previous chapter we described the binomial and Poisson distributions. These distributions have one important feature in common: the possible values that the random variable they describe can take on are countable. As you know, distributions with this property are called *discrete*. The continuous distributions that we discuss next do not have this property. They can take on any value within some interval of the real line. (There is a third category of distributions that can take on values in two distinct sets, one countable the other not. These are called *mixed*. We do not consider them in detail here.) The uniform (or rectangular), exponential, gamma, beta and normal distributions discussed here are examples of such continuous distributions. Since such distributions describe the continuous type of random variables discussed earlier in this chapter we may apply the techniques and concepts developed for their analysis. More specifically, the calculation of any probability associated with a given domain of the random variable involves the integration of continuous functions rather than the summation of discrete expressions.

Many of the distributions we shall be discussing are related in important and interesting ways. In the course of our discussion we will endeavour to highlight these interrelationships. The computer software that accompanies the text is particularly important in this respect.

3.5 THE UNIFORM OR RECTANGULAR DISTRIBUTION

As shown in Program 23, the uniform or rectangular distribution assigns equal probability to equal subintervals of its domain. In principle such a distribution is useful in modelling many random events where the outcome is uncertain but where any specific value of the random variable is as likely as any other. For example, in bingo or a lottery before the play starts the likelihood of any specific number should be equal to that of any other number which could be drawn. Indeed it is on this basis that such betting can be regarded as fair, namely an equal *a priori* chance of success. The uniform or rectangular distribution can be defined over any connected interval on the real line $[\alpha, \beta]$. Therefore, we can define the uniform density formally in the following way. (Fig. 3.7 which accompanies the formulas for the density and cumulative distribution functions gives the shapes of these two functions.)

Definition 3.5.1 A random variable X is *uniformly* distributed over the interval (α, β) if its probability density function is given by Fig. 3.7a.

Example 3.5.1 The direction measured in degrees from due north in which a well-balanced spinner points when it comes to rest will have a rectangular distribution over the interval $[0, 360]$. This density function has the rectangular shape indicated in the computer programs.

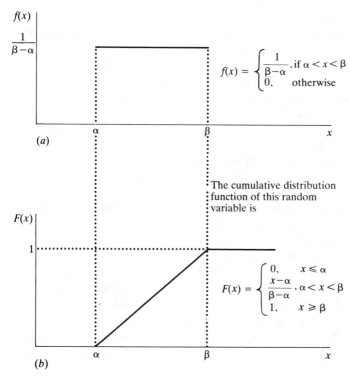

$$f(x) = \begin{cases} \dfrac{1}{\beta-\alpha}, & \text{if } \alpha < x < \beta \\ 0, & \text{otherwise} \end{cases}$$

The cumulative distribution function of this random variable is

$$F(x) = \begin{cases} 0, & x \leq \alpha \\ \dfrac{x-\alpha}{\beta-\alpha}, & \alpha < x < \beta \\ 1, & x \geq \beta \end{cases}$$

Figure 3.7

Example 3.5.2 If X is uniformly distributed as $(0, 10)$, calculate $P(X < 3)$ and $P(1 < X < 8)$.

$$P\{X < 3\} = \int_0^3 \tfrac{1}{10} \, dx = \tfrac{3}{10} \qquad P\{3 < X < 8\} = \int_3^8 \tfrac{1}{10} \, dx = \tfrac{1}{2}$$

3.6 THE NORMAL DISTRIBUTION

The next special continuous distribution to be considered is the most widely used of all, and our discussion is correspondingly more detailed. The reason for its central place in statistics arises from the fact that large numbers of random influences acting independently tend, in aggregate, to be normally distributed. This fact is given a precise statement in the central limit theorem, which is illustrated in Program 27.5 and in the companion Book 3 of *Statistics in Action* on statistical inference. Here we briefly sketch the meaning of the central limit theorem in an attempt to convince the reader that the normal distribution is a useful tool

Consider the heights of women in a large population. The height of an individual woman is determined by many different factors including the genes given her by her parents, diet, exercise, geographical location, incidence of disease during her childhood, etc. Each of these factors can operate independently; that is the fact that someone lives in Salt Lake City does not necessarily imply that they get more or less exercise than a person living elsewhere in the world. The central limit theorem can be interpreted to mean that because there are a large number of independent influences acting on the height of women we should expect to find that heights are normally distributed. Is it true that the heights of people in a population are approximately normally distributed? The answer is yes.

The second reason for the importance of the normal distribution is rather more technical in nature, but has important practical consequences. In many situations, it is possible to save work by using the normal distribution where the binomial or the Poisson may, strictly speaking, be more appropriate. This is because in certain circumstances (to be detailed below), these distributions can be approximated accurately by the normal. This can save work because the normal distribution is generally easier and quicker to use than the discrete distributions. This second aspect of the normal distribution is illustrated in Programs 27.3 and 27.4 and is given a more formal analysis at the end of this chapter. We begin our discussion with a statement of the normal density function. Programs 27.1 and 27.2 refer to this discussion.

Definition 3.6.1 X is a *normally distributed* random variable with mean μ and variance σ^2 is the probability density function of X if

$$f(x) = \frac{1}{\sqrt{2\pi}\sigma}e^{-(x-\mu)^2/(2\sigma^2)} \qquad -\infty < x < \infty$$

This distribution has a characteristic 'bell' shape and can be drawn as shown in Fig. 3.8. The proof that such a function is a probability density

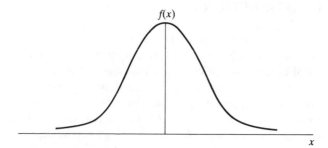

$f(x)$

x

Figure 3.8

function is not straightforward and will be returned to later.

As explained in the computer program, μ and σ are parameters of a family of distributions. These distributions all have the famous 'bell' shape. It is a special and remarkable feature of the normal distributions that each member of the family is related to the other by a simple transformation.

Consider, for instance, the effect on a random variable X which is normally distributed with mean μ and variance σ^2 of subtracting a constant, c. The distribution function of $X - c$ is

$$F_{X-c}(x) = P(X - c \leqslant x) = P(X \leqslant x + c)$$
$$= \int_{-\infty}^{x+c} f_X(t)\, dt$$

where f_X is the density function of X. It follows that the density function is

$$f_{X-c}(x) = \frac{d}{dx} F_{X-c}(x)$$
$$= \frac{d}{dx} \int_{-\infty}^{x+c} f_X(t)\, dt$$
$$= f_X(x + c)$$

This is the density function of a normally distributed random variable with mean $\mu - c$ and variance σ^2. To see this, write out $f(x + c)$ in full:

$$f_X(x + c) = \frac{1}{2\pi\sigma^2} \exp\left[\frac{1}{2} \left(\frac{x + c - \mu}{\sigma} \right)^2 \right]$$
$$= \frac{1}{2\pi\sigma^2} \exp\left\{ \frac{1}{2} \left[\frac{x - (\mu - c)}{\sigma} \right]^2 \right\}$$

We conclude that subtracting a constant from a normally distributed random variable simply has the effect of creating a new random variable whose density function is a translation of the original density function.

Second, consider dividing X by a constant $c > 0$. The distribution function of X/c is

$$F_{X/c}(x) = P\left(\frac{X}{c} \leqslant x \right) = P(X \leqslant cx)$$
$$= \int_{-\infty}^{cx} f_X(t)\, dt$$

The density function is therefore

$$f_{X/c}(x) = \frac{d}{dx} \int_{-\infty}^{cx} f_X(t)\, dt$$
$$= c f_X(cx)$$

$$= \frac{c}{2\pi\sigma^2} \exp\left[\frac{1}{2}\left(\frac{cx - \mu}{\sigma}\right)^2\right]$$

$$= \frac{1}{2\pi(\sigma/c)^2} \exp\left[\frac{1}{2}\left(\frac{x - \mu/c}{\sigma/c}\right)^2\right]$$

This is simply the density of a normally distributed random variable with mean μ/c and standard deviation σ/c. A similar argument can be used for the case where $c < 0$.

It follows from these facts that a given normally distributed random variable can be transformed into a normally distributed random variable with a different mean and/or standard deviation simply by dividing by an appropriate constant and subtracting another appropriate constant (i.e. by applying a linear transformation). This is summarized in the following theorem.

Theorem 3.6.1 If X is a random variable with the $N(\mu, \sigma^2)$ distribution, then $X + c$ has the $N(\mu + c, \sigma^2)$ distribution and X/c has the $N(\mu/c, \sigma^2/c^2)$ distribution.

Corollary 3.6.1 If X is a random variable with the $N(\mu, \sigma^2)$ distribution and b and c are any constants, then $bX + c$ has the normal distribution $N(b\mu + c, b^2\sigma^2)$.

The fact that linear transformations of normal random variables yield random variables with an easily calculated distribution is a feature of the normal distribution that makes it easy to work with in practice. The distribution does have one unpleasant feature, however, which is that it is not possible to integrate the density function explicitly except by numerical methods. These numerical methods are typically long-winded and cumbersome (they involve adding up the areas of large numbers of rectangles), but the recent development of cheap and quick computing devices has made them feasible for everyday use. Traditionally, the problem of computing probabilities from the normal density function has been tackled by making use of the fact that the members of the normal family are related by linear transformations. This means that it is only necessary explicitly to calculate the integrals of one member of the family. The integrals of other members can then be obtained by applying the appropriate transformation. The normal distribution whose integrals are usually tabulated is the member of the family with $\mu = 0$ and $\sigma^2 = 1$. This is known as the *standard normal distribution*. We may state this as a formal result.

Theorem 3.6.2 If X is a random variable with the $\sim N(\mu, \sigma^2)$ distribution, $\sigma^2 > 0$, then the random variable

$$Z = \left(\frac{X - \mu}{\sigma}\right) \text{ is } N(0, 1)$$

PROOF The cumulative distribution function $F(z)$ of Z is

$$F(z) = P\left(\frac{X - \mu}{\sigma} \leqslant z\right) = P(X \leqslant z\sigma + \mu)$$

$$= \int_{-\infty}^{z\sigma + \mu} \frac{1}{\sigma\sqrt{2\pi}} \exp\left[-\frac{(x - \mu)^2}{2\sigma^2}\right] dx$$

Changing the variable of integration by writing $y = (x - \mu)/\sigma$, then

$$F(z) = \int_{-\infty}^{z} \frac{1}{\sqrt{2\pi}} e^{-y^2/2} dy$$

Since $f(z) = F'(z)$, then

$$f(z) = \frac{1}{\sqrt{2\pi}} e^{-z^2/2} \qquad -\infty < z < \infty$$

Thus Z has the $\sim N(0, 1)$ distribution.

The c.d.f. of the standard normal is often denoted by Φ. Theorem 3.6.1 is a very useful property since it means that for any normally distributed random variable we can compute the probability associated with a range of values by using only the standard normal probability table.

What is the appropriate transformation that should be applied to a member of the normal family with mean μ and variance σ^2? The answer can be inferred from Theorem 3.6.2. If the given random variable has variance σ^2 and we want to derive a random variable with variance 1 we have to divide by σ. If we want to shift the mean of a random variable with mean μ to zero, we must subtract μ. Thus, if we want to compute

$$P(X \leqslant x) = \int_{-\infty}^{x} \frac{1}{2\pi\sigma^2} \exp\left[\frac{1}{2}\left(\frac{t - \mu}{\sigma}\right)^2\right] dt$$

we observe that

$$P(X \leqslant x) = P\left(\frac{X - \mu}{\sigma} \leqslant \frac{x - \mu}{\sigma}\right)$$

$$= \int_{-\infty}^{-(x - \mu)/\sigma} \frac{1}{\sqrt{2\pi}} \exp\left(\frac{t^2}{2}\right) dt$$

The values of this integral are in the tables given in Appendix B for $(X - \mu)/\sigma$ between 0 and ∞. These are the only values we need, since integrals for $(X - \mu)/\sigma$ between 0 and $-\infty$ can be obtained from the tabulated values by exploiting the symmetry of the normal distribution and the fact that it integrates to unity along the whole real line.

Theorem 3.6.3 $\Phi(-x) = 1 - \Phi(x)$

PROOF Follows directly from the symmetry of the density function and is left as an exercise.

Example 3.6.1 If we require

$$P\left(\frac{X - \mu}{\sigma} \leqslant -0.3\right)$$

we can write this as

$$1 - P\left(\frac{X - \mu}{\sigma} \geqslant -0.3\right) = 1 - P\left(\frac{X - \mu}{\sigma} \leqslant 0.3\right)$$

It is also possible to find the probability that a normally distributed random variable takes a value in a given interval. Consider a random variable X with parameters μ and σ; then Z is the appropriate standard normal random variable. Thus to find $P(a < X < b)$ note that

$$P(a < X < b) = P\left(\frac{a - \mu}{\sigma} < \frac{X - \mu}{\sigma} < \frac{b - \mu}{\sigma}\right)$$

$$= P\left(\frac{a - \mu}{\sigma} < Z < \frac{b - \mu}{\sigma}\right)$$

Example 3.6.2 If X is $N(3, 9)$ find $P\{2 < X < 5\}$, $P\{X > 0\}$.

$$P\{2 < X < 5\} = P\{-\tfrac{1}{3} < Z < \tfrac{2}{3}\} = \Phi(\tfrac{2}{3}) - \Phi(-\tfrac{1}{3})$$
$$= \Phi(\tfrac{2}{3}) - [1 - \Phi(\tfrac{1}{3})]$$
$$= .3779$$
$$P\{X > 0\} = P\{Z > -1\} = 1 - \Phi(-1) = \Phi(1)$$
$$= .8413$$

We remarked earlier that this method of using tables to calculate probabilities for normally distributed random variables is 'traditional'. Recall that the only reason for the tables is the difficulty of using numerical methods for the computation of the necessary integrals. Fast, cheap computing has changed the feasibility of lengthy calculations, which can now be done routinely to any desired degree of accuracy.

Program 27.6 is a routine that will provide probabilities for the lower tail of any normally distributed random variable very quickly and to an accuracy of five decimal places. Probabilities for intervals and the upper tail can be computed from the lower-tail probabilities in the manner described above.

A fact that will be needed frequently in our discussion of estimation and hypothesis testing is that the sum of two independent, normally distributed random variables is normally distributed with the mean equal to the sum of the means and the variance equal to the sum of the variances. The proof of this result is most easily shown using moment generating functions. Since these are not introduced until Chapter 5 the proof of the following theorem is presented there.

Theorem 3.6.4 If X_1 has the $N(\mu_1, \sigma_1^2)$ distribution and X_2 has the $N(\mu_2, \sigma_2^2)$ distribution and these random variables are independent, then $X_1 + X_2$ has the $N(\mu_1 + \mu_2, \sigma_1^2 + \sigma_1^2)$ distribution.

Finally, for reference, we repeat the argument given in Program 27.3 about how the normal distribution can be used to approximate the binomial when n is large. The argument has two steps. First an approximation to the discrete distribution is developed. This represents the distribution approximately as a function on the real line. The second stage of the argument shows that this function approximates a normal density function more and more closely as n increases.

The outcome of a Bernoulli trial can be represented as a random variable with density

$$P(X = x) = f(x) = p^x(1-p)^{(1-x)} \qquad x = 0, 1$$

The mean of this random variable is p and its variance is $p(1-p)$. A sequence of independent random variables of this type will each be either a one or a zero. Their mean will be the proportion of successes in the sequence

$$\bar{x} = \frac{1}{n} \sum X_i$$

The distribution of the mean $\bar{x}$ is discrete. It takes on the values $\bar{x} = 0, 1/n, 2/n, \ldots, n/n$ with associated probabilities $g(\bar{x})$. This distribution can be represented graphically by constructing for each value of $\bar{x}$ a rectangle of height $g(\bar{x})$ and width $1/n$ centred at $\bar{x}$. The tops of these rectangles then form a step function, the area under which is $1/n$ [since $\Sigma g(\bar{x}) = 1$].

As n becomes larger the steps in the function become progressively smaller. In the limit as n approaches infinity this function (multiplied by n) approaches a normal distribution. Call this function $h(\bar{x})$. The probabilities $g(x)$ and the function $h(x)$ are illustrated in Figs. 3.9 and 3.10.

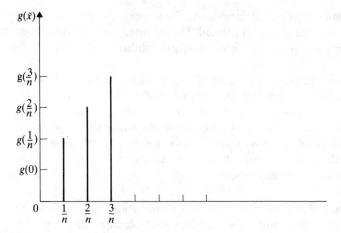

Figure 3.9

Now consider non-negative integers a and b where $a \leqslant b \leqslant n$. We can calculate the probability that $\bar{x}$ lies in the interval $(a/n, b/n)$ in two different ways. First, we can use the binomial density $g(\bar{x})$:

$$P\left(\frac{a}{n} \leqslant x \leqslant \frac{b}{n}\right) = \sum_{x=a/n}^{b/n} g(\bar{x}) = \sum_{j=a}^{b} \binom{n}{j} p^j (1-p)^{(n-j)}$$

Second, we can use the function $h(\bar{x})$ and integrate it over the appropriate interval:

$$P\left(\frac{a}{n} \leqslant \bar{x} \leqslant \frac{b}{n}\right) = n \int_{(a-\frac{1}{2})/n}^{(b+\frac{1}{2})/n} h(t)\, dt$$

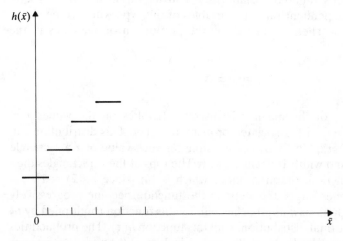

Figure 3.10

Since $nh(\bar{x})$ approaches a normal density as n gets larger, the integral in the second equation will become closer to an integral of a normal density. Thus for large values of n the binomial probabilities in the first equation will be close to the normal probabilities.

What practical use are these facts? The answer is that they can save a lot of work in calculating probabilities. The next example shows how.

Example 3.6.3 A quality control inspection is under way in which an acceptable proportion of defective items is $\frac{1}{5}$. A sample of 500 is taken and there are 120 defective items in the sample. Is this evidence to suggest that the proportion of defectives in the output as a whole is greater than $\frac{1}{5}$, or is it simply bad luck that the proportion of defectives in the sample turned out to be so high?

To answer this question we can calculate the probability that the number of defectives deviates from the expected number by 20 or more. Using binomial probabilities this involves working out the following expression, which is not simple:

$$p(80 \leqslant j \leqslant 120) = \sum_{80}^{120} \binom{500}{j} 0.2^{j} 0.8^{500-j}$$

The same job can be done using the normal approximation. We know that

$$p(80 \leqslant j \leqslant 120) = P\left(\frac{80}{500} \leqslant \bar{x} \leqslant \frac{120}{500}\right)$$

$$= P\left(\frac{\frac{80}{500} - \frac{1}{5}}{\frac{1}{5} \times \frac{4}{5} \times \frac{1}{500}} \leqslant \frac{x - \frac{1}{5}}{\frac{1}{5} \times \frac{4}{5} \times \frac{1}{500}} \leqslant \frac{\frac{120}{500} - \frac{1}{5}}{\frac{1}{5} \times \frac{4}{5} \times \frac{1}{500}}\right)$$

Since

$$y = \left[\frac{x - \frac{1}{5}}{\frac{1}{5} \times \frac{4}{5} \times \frac{1}{500}}\right]$$

is approximately standard normally distributed, we can compute this probability easily from the tables:

$$P(-2.24 \leqslant y \leqslant 2.24) = .9875 - .0125 = .9750$$

The normal distribution can also be used to approximate the Poisson distribution. Since the Poisson distribution can be viewed as a limiting version of the binomial as n becomes large and p becomes small, and since the binomial can be approximated by the normal for large values of n, it follows that the Poisson can be approximated by the normal for large values of λ. In order to get some feel for how these approximations work and how good they are for different parameter values, you should look at Program 27.4.

Exercises 3.6

Exercise 3.6.1 Using the tables (Appendix B), calculate the following probabilities for a random variable X with $\mu = 0$ and $\sigma^2 = 1$:
(a) $P(x \leqslant 0.5)$ (c) $P(x \leqslant 1)$
(b) $P(x \leqslant -0.5)$ (d) $P(x \leqslant -0.2)$

Exercise 3.6.2 Calculate the same probabilities listed in Exercise 3.6.1 for a random variable X with $\mu = 0.2$ and $\sigma^2 = 0.49$.

Exercise 3.6.3 Using the tables (Appendix B), calculate the following probabilities for a random variable X with $\mu = 100$ and $\sigma^2 = 10000$.
(a) $P(X > 150)$ (e) $P(X > 160 \text{ or } X \leqslant 40)$
(b) $P(X \leqslant 25)$ (f) $P(X > -30)$
(c) $P(37 \leqslant X < 104)$ (g) $P(X > 25 \text{ and } X < 75)$
(d) $P(X > 75)$ (h) $P(X > 25 \text{ and } X > 75)$

Exercise 3.6.4 The diameters of the bolts in a large box follow a normal distribution with a mean of 2 cm and a variance of .009 cm^2. Another large box contains nuts whose internal diameters follow a normal distribution with a mean of 2.02 cm and a variance of .016 cm^2.

A bolt and a nut can be used together if the diameter of the nut is larger than the diameter of the bolt and the difference between them is no greater than 0.05 cm. If a bolt and a nut are chosen at random what is the probability that they can be used together?

Exercise 3.6.5 Lognormal. The lognormal distribution is often used in the study of income distribution because it seems to fit observed income distributions quite well. X is said to have a lognormal distribution if $\log X$ has a normal distribution. Suppose $E(\log X) = \mu$ and $\text{var}(\log X) = \sigma^2$. What is the density function of X? Sketch the density.

3.7 EXPONENTIAL, GAMMA AND χ^2 DISTRIBUTIONS

These three distributions are closely related to each other and to the normal. The main goal of this section is to explain the relationships between random variables with these densities. We begin with the exponential distribution. This distribution can be formally defined by writing down its probability density function.

Definition 3.7.1 An *exponential* random variable X has a probability density function (p.d.f.) for some parameter $\lambda > 0$ given by

$$f(x) = \begin{cases} \lambda e^{-\lambda x} & \text{if } x \geq 0 \\ 0 & \text{if } x < 0 \end{cases}$$

Note that this random variable is always positive.

The shape of this random variable is conditional on the value of λ as indicated below in Fig. 3.11 and Program 25.

The cumulative distribution function of the exponential distribution is

$$F(a) = P\{X \leq a\}$$

$$\int_0^a \lambda e^{-\lambda x}\, dx$$

$$= [-e^{-\lambda x}]_0^a$$

$$= 1 - e^{-\lambda a} \qquad a \geq 0$$

Later we will show that the parameter λ is the reciprocal of the expectation of the random variable.

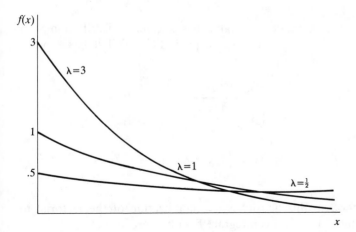

Figure 3.11

Example 3.7.1 Let X denote the length of a phone call in minutes. Assume X is exponentially distributed with $\lambda = \frac{1}{5}$. Find $P\{X > 5\}$, $P\{5 < X < 15\}$.

$$P\{X > 5\} = \int_5^\infty \tfrac{1}{5} e^{-x/5}\, dx = [-e^{-x/5}]_5^\infty = e^{-1} \approx .368$$

$$P\{5 < X < 15\} = \int_5^{15} \tfrac{1}{5} e^{-x/5}\, dx = [-e^{-x/5}]_5^{15}$$

$$= e^{-1} - e^{-3} \approx .318$$

The distribution is often used in modelling elapsed time before some event occurs. For instance, the length of time between the arrivals of successive customers at a shop counter or hospital admission desk can be modelled using the exponential distribution. In fact, the distribution has a close relationship to the Poisson distribution.

In the Geiger counter example in Chapter 2, we showed that the number of particles hitting the counter in any given period of time would follow a Poisson distribution. It is also true that the length of time between two successive particles has an exponential distribution and that the waiting time until the next particle arrives has an exponential distribution. The proof of some of these facts is the subject of Exercise 3.7.4.

The exponential distribution is a special case of the gamma distribution. In its turn the gamma distribution has the χ^2 distribution as a special case. This latter distribution is very useful in statistical inference and in distribution theory since it is the distribution of a squared standard normal deviate. It is for this reason that we introduce the gamma distribution at this point.

Definition 3.7.2 A random variable has a *gamma* distribution with parameters (λ, α), $\alpha > 0$ and $\lambda > 0$ [X is $\Gamma(\lambda, \alpha)$] if it has a probability density function given by

$$f(x) = \begin{cases} \dfrac{\alpha e^{-\alpha x}(\alpha x)^{\lambda-1}}{\Gamma(\lambda)} & x \geq 0 \\ 0 & x < 0 \end{cases}$$

where

$$\Gamma(\lambda) = \int_0^\infty e^{-y} y^{\lambda-1}\, dy$$

The Γ-integral in this density is a generalization of the factorial to non-integer values. To see this integrate $\Gamma(\lambda)$ by parts to get

$$\Gamma(\lambda) = [-e^{-y}y^{\lambda-1}]_0^\infty + \int_0^\infty e^{-y}(\lambda-1)y^{\lambda-2}\, dy$$

$$= (\lambda-1)\int_0^\infty e^{-y}y^{\lambda-2}\, dy$$

$$= (\lambda-1)\Gamma(\lambda-1)$$

By repeated integration with $\lambda = n$,

$$\Gamma(n) = (n-1)\Gamma(n-1)$$
$$= (n-1)(n-2)\Gamma(n-2)$$
$$= (n-1)(n-2)\ldots 3.2\Gamma(1)$$

Since
$$\Gamma(1) = \int_0^\infty e^{-x}\,dx = 1$$
$$\Gamma(n) = (n-1)!$$

The gamma distribution with parameters (λ, α) often arises as the distribution of the amount of time one has to wait until a total of n events has occurred. In such cases, λ would take on the integer value n. In the context of this interpretation we can see that the gamma distribution should be related to the exponential distribution, since the latter is the distribution of the elapsed time before a single event occurs. More precisely the gamma distribution has the exponential as the special case when $\lambda = 1$ in the above density. The interpretation of gamma distributed random variables as waiting times also suggested that the sum of independent gamma random variables should be gamma distributed. That this is indeed the case is shown in Exercise 3.7.2.

Two examples of the gamma density are graphed in the Figure 3.12 for the case where $\alpha = 1$ and $\lambda = \frac{1}{2}$ and where $\alpha = 1$ and $\lambda = 2$.

The last fact that we need to know about gamma distributed random variables is given in the following theorem.

Theorem 3.7.1 If X is a gamma distributed random variable with parameters λ and α, then cX is also gamma distributed, with parameters λ and α/c.

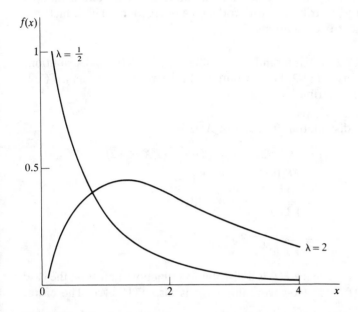

Figure 3.12

PROOF The distribution function of cX is

$$F(z) = P(cX \leqslant z) = P(X \leqslant z/c)$$
$$= \int_0^{z/c} \frac{\alpha e^{-\alpha x} (\alpha x)^{(\lambda-1)}}{\Gamma(\lambda)} \, dx$$

Therefore

$$f(z) = \frac{dF(z)}{dz} = \frac{1}{c} \frac{\alpha e^{-\alpha(z/c)} (\alpha z/c)^{(\lambda-1)}}{\Gamma(\lambda)}$$

which is the density function of a random variable with the $\Gamma(\lambda, \alpha/c)$ distribution.

We can now turn to the χ^2 distribution.

Definition 3.7.3 A random variable with the $\Gamma(k/2, 1/2)$ distribution (that is $\lambda = k/2$ and $\alpha = 1/2$) is said to have a χ^2 distribution with k degrees of freedom, $\chi^2(k)$.

This form of the gamma distribution plays a central role in statistical theory because the square of a standard normally distributed random variable has a χ^2 distribution with one degree of freedom. It follows from the additivity of independent gamma distributed random variables that the sum of squares of n independent standard normally distributed random variables has a χ^2 distribution with n degrees of freedom. These facts are shown in the next two theorems.

Theorem 3.7.2 If X is a random variable with the $N(0, 1)$ distribution, then $X^2/2$ has a $\Gamma(1/2, 1)$ distribution. Furthermore, X^2 has a $\Gamma(1/2, 1/2)$ or $\chi^2(1)$ distribution.

PROOF The distribution function of $X^2/2$ is

$$F(t) = P(X^2/2 \leqslant t) = P(-\sqrt{2t} \leqslant X \leqslant \sqrt{2t})$$
$$= 2P(0 \leqslant X \leqslant \sqrt{2t})$$
$$= \frac{2}{\sqrt{2\pi}} \int_0^{\sqrt{2t}} \exp\left(\frac{-x^2}{2}\right) dx$$
$$= \frac{1}{\sqrt{\pi}} \int_0^{t} y^{-1/2} e^{-y} \, dy$$

where $y = x^2/2$. Since $F(t)$ is a distribution function it must be the case that $\lim_{t \to \infty} F(t) = 1$. However, this limit is also $\Gamma(1/2)/\sqrt{\pi}$. Therefore, we have shown that $X^2/2$ has a $\Gamma(1/2, 1)$ distribution and, as a by-product, that $\Gamma(1/2) = \sqrt{\pi}$. Since $X^2/2$ has a $\Gamma(1/2, 1)$ distribution, Theorem 3.7.1 implies that X^2 has a $\chi^2(1)$ distribution, and the theorem is proved.

We are now in a position to prove a further important theorem, which justifies the importance of the χ^2 distribution in statistics.

Theorem 3.7.3 If $X_1, \ldots, X_n$ are independent random variables each with the $N(0, 1)$ distribution, then the sum of squares $X_1^2 + \cdots + X_i^2$ has a $\chi^2(n)$ distribution.

PROOF By Theorem 3.7.2, each X_i^2 has a $\chi^2(1)$ distribution. Then additivity of gamma variates (Exercise 3.7.4) implies the required result.

Exercises 3.7

Exercise 3.7.1 Sketch the density functions of gamma distributed random variables with the following parameters:
   (a) $\alpha = \frac{1}{2}; \beta = 1$ (b) $\alpha = 1; \beta = 1$ (c) $\alpha = 2; \beta = 1$
Where do the modes of these distributions lie?

Exercise 3.7.2 The life of a lightbulb is exponentially distributed with mean $1/\lambda$. A house is equipped with 30 new lightbulbs.
   (a) How long should the owner expect to be able to live in the house before having to replace a bulb?
   (b) Suppose $\lambda = 1/700$ days. What is the probability that he will have to buy a new bulb within a year?

Exercise 3.7.3 A set of random variables $X_1, \ldots, X_k$ are independent and X_i has an exponential distribution with parameter $\beta_i, i = 1, \ldots, k$. Let $Y = \min(X_1, \ldots, X_k)$. Show that Y has an exponential distribution with parameter $\Sigma \beta_i$.
   Hint: $P(Y \geqslant y) = P(X_1 \geqslant y)P(X_2 \geqslant y) \cdots P(X_k \geqslant y)$.

Exercise 3.7.4 Gamma and exponential. We have noted that the exponential distribution with parameter λ is the same as a $\Gamma(1, \lambda)$ distribution. It is also true that sum of n independent exponentially distributed random variables each with the same parameter λ is $\Gamma(n, \lambda)$. Using the techniques of Sec. 4.4, show that the sum of two independent exponentially distributed random variables has a $\Gamma(2, \lambda)$ distribution.

Exercise 3.7.5 Gamma and Poisson. The length of time taken to answer an enquiry at a Post Office counter is exponentially distributed with parameter λ. Assuming enquiries to be mutually independent, show that the number of enquiries handled in a given time period t has a Poisson distribution with parameter λt.

Hint: Let the length of the ith enquiry be X_i. Then the event $Y = n$ is the same as the event

$$\sum_1^n X_i \leqslant t \quad \text{and} \quad \sum_1^{n+1} X_i > t$$

Show that this implies that

$$P(Y = n) = P\left(\sum_1^n X_i \leqslant t\right) - P\left(\sum_1^{n+1} X_i \leqslant t\right)$$

The probabilities on the right-hand side are gamma. Integrate the second of them by parts, to conclude that

$$P(Y = n) = \frac{(\lambda t)^n \, e^{-\lambda t}}{n!}$$

*3.8 THE BETA DISTRIBUTION

For completeness, we add a brief description of the beta distribution. This distribution is very useful in the modelling of random variables that have upper and lower bounds on their domain but may take a variety of symmetric or skew-symmetric shapes. By the appropriate use of the parameters in the beta distribution it is possible to generate many different shapes for this distribution.

Definition 3.8.1 A random variable X has a *beta* distribution if its density is given by

$$f(x) = \begin{cases} \dfrac{1}{\mathrm{B}(a,b)} x^{a-1}(1-x)^{b-1} & 0 < x < 1 \\ 0 & \text{otherwise} \end{cases}$$

where

$$\mathrm{B}(a,b) = \int_0^1 x^{a-1}(1-x)^{b-1} \, \mathrm{d}x$$

The beta distribution represents random variables defined over a finite interval $[c, d]$, and its shape is governed by the values of the parameters α

and β as indicated in Figs 3.13 and 3.14. When $a = b$ the beta density is symmetric about $\frac{1}{2}$, giving more weight to the tails as a decreases. When $b > a$ the density is skewed to the left and if $a > b$ it is skewed to the right. In Fig. 3.14 are drawn the beta densities with parameters (a, b) when $a \neq b$ for various values.

Although we do not prove it here, it is a fact that if X and Y are gamma distributed and independent, then $X/(X + Y)$ has a beta distribution.

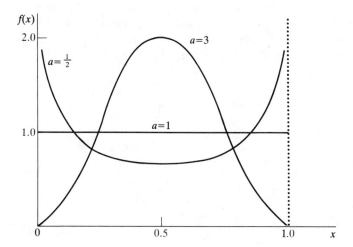

Figure 3.13

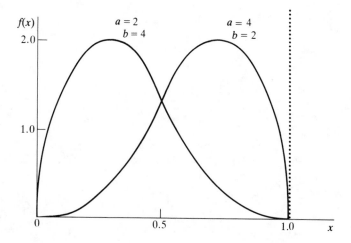

Figure 3.14

Exercises 3.8

Exercise 3.8.1 Sketch the density functions of beta distributed random variables with the following parameters:

(a) $\alpha = \frac{1}{2}$; $\beta = \frac{1}{2}$ (b) $\alpha = \frac{1}{2}$; $\beta = 1$

(c) $\alpha = \frac{1}{2}$; $\beta = 2$ (d) $\alpha = 1$; $\beta = 1$

(e) $\alpha = 2$; $\beta = 2$ (f) $\alpha = 25$; $\beta = 100$

Exercise 3.8.2 Large consignments of motor spares have a proportion X of defective items, where X is a beta distributed random variable with parameters α and β. If two items are selected at random from a consignment, what is the probability that they are both defective?

FOUR
JOINTLY DISTRIBUTED RANDOM VARIABLES

4.1 INTRODUCTION

So far in this text we have considered only single random variables; e.g. the score with one arrow in an archery contest or the arrival time of a British Rail train. In practice we are often interested in the simultaneous occurrence of more than one random phenomenon. For example, a medical statistician may be interested in both the height *and* weight of a patient, an economist may be interested in what values of consumption and income simultaneously occur and an educational selector may be interested in the association between a pre-university educational test and the performance at college. Each of these examples is a situation in which more than one random variable must be studied at a time. In such situations the random variables may be jointly determined and we therefore seek to examine the joint probability distribution which describes the occurrence of any pair of X, Y random variables. Naturally it is possible to extend our study to the analysis of more than two random variables, i.e. to multivariate distributions. Although in this particular chapter we concentrate on joint or bivariate distributions most of the concepts and results carry over without difficulty to the case of multivariate distributions. In addition a study of bivariate distributions is sufficient to equip us with the concepts necessary to analyse prediction problems, problems of independence and association and aspects of statistical inference to be met later.

Table 4.1

d_2	d_1					
	1	2	3	4	5	6
1	(1,1)	(1,2)	(1,3)	(1,4)	(1,5)	(1,6)
2	(2,1)	(2,2)	(2,3)	(2,4)	(2,5)	(2,6)
3	(3,1)	(3,2)	(3,3)	(3,4)	(3,5)	(3,6)
4	(4,1)	(4,2)	(4,3)	(4,4)	(4,5)	(4,6)
5	(5,1)	(5,2)	(5,3)	(5,4)	(5,5)	(5,6)
6	(6,1)	(6,2)	(6,3)	(6,4)	(6,5)	(6,6)

4.2 JOINTLY DISTRIBUTED RANDOM VARIABLES

In order to illustrate the concepts associated with joint distributions we will study one example in some detail. (This example is also explored in Program 29.) Consider again our example of throwing two dice. Previously we considered a random variable in this experiment to be the sum of the numbers on the two dice. Now let us consider the number on each die to be a separate random variable. We can tabulate the possible values that the two dice may take in Table 4.1, where the first number in each pair, d_2, denotes the number on the die and the second number in the pair, d_1, denotes the number on the other die. We can now consider the random variable, X, to be the number of spots showing on the first die and the random variable, Y, to be the number of spots showing on the second die.

The joint probability function associated with the pairs of the random variables X, Y can easily be computed. From Table 4.1 we can see that there are 36 possible outcomes to this experiment. We may denote the probability associated with each outcome as a function $f(x, y)$ which specifies for each pair of possible outcomes what the probability associated with that outcome is. Since each outcome in this experiment is equally likely then $f(X, Y) = 1/36$. It is possible to represent this joint probability function by a table. The table corresponding to the sample space above is given in Table 4.2. Thus the probability of $X = 3$ and $Y = 2$ is given by the element in the third row and third column of Table 4.2.

As in the univariate case there are several important logical properties which this joint distribution must satisfy, namely that the probability associated with each cell must be greater than or equal to zero and that the total sum of the probability associated with all possible values of x and y must be unity.

The joint probability function provides us with the information that relates to any pair of x, y values in combination. However, we may also be interested in the probabilities associated with x regardless of the value

Table 4.2

x	y						$f_X(x)$
	1	2	3	4	5	6	
1	$\frac{1}{36}$	$\frac{1}{36}$	$\frac{1}{36}$	$\frac{1}{36}$	$\frac{1}{36}$	$\frac{1}{36}$	$\frac{1}{6}$
2	$\frac{1}{36}$	$\frac{1}{36}$	$\frac{1}{36}$	$\frac{1}{36}$	$\frac{1}{36}$	$\frac{1}{36}$	$\frac{1}{6}$
3	$\frac{1}{36}$	$\frac{1}{36}$	$\frac{1}{36}$	$\frac{1}{36}$	$\frac{1}{36}$	$\frac{1}{36}$	$\frac{1}{6}$
4	$\frac{1}{36}$	$\frac{1}{36}$	$\frac{1}{36}$	$\frac{1}{36}$	$\frac{1}{36}$	$\frac{1}{36}$	$\frac{1}{6}$
5	$\frac{1}{36}$	$\frac{1}{36}$	$\frac{1}{36}$	$\frac{1}{36}$	$\frac{1}{36}$	$\frac{1}{36}$	$\frac{1}{6}$
6	$\frac{1}{36}$	$\frac{1}{36}$	$\frac{1}{36}$	$\frac{1}{36}$	$\frac{1}{36}$	$\frac{1}{36}$	$\frac{1}{6}$
$f_Y(y)$	$\frac{1}{6}$	$\frac{1}{6}$	$\frac{1}{6}$	$\frac{1}{6}$	$\frac{1}{6}$	$\frac{1}{6}$	

taken by y or the probabilities associated with y regardless of the values taken by x. Such a univariate function is called a *marginal probability function* and can be derived from the joint probability function by simply summing across the rows (to find the marginal probability function of x) or down the columns (to find the marginal probability function of y). For example, if we wished to compute the probability that $X = 1$ we would have to sum all the probabilities associated with $X = 1$, that is

$$P(X = 1) = f(1,1) + f(1,2) + f(1,3) + f(1,4) + f(1,5) + f(1,6)$$

which in this case is $\frac{1}{36} + \frac{1}{36} + \frac{1}{36} + \frac{1}{36} + \frac{1}{36} + \frac{1}{36} = \frac{1}{6}$.

Other marginal probabilities can be computed in an analogous way. In this example the marginal probability functions are given by the last column (for x) and the last row (for y). These marginal probability functions are univariate probability functions in the usual sense as defined in the previous chapter. Therefore, as one would expect for consistency, the sum of the marginal probabilities over all possible values is also unity.

Another important concept may now be introduced in this example. Two random variables are said to be *independent* if the probability of the joint occurrence of $X = x$ and $Y = y$ can be computed by multiplying the probability of $X = x$ occurring and $Y = y$ occurring separately. This needs to be true for all possible pairs of values of x and y. If two random variables are not independent they are said to be *dependent*. Referring to the example above we can see that X and Y in this case are independent. This can be seen intuitively since the probability of throwing a specific number on one dice is totally unrelated to throwing another specific number on the second dice. Therefore the probability of throwing any given pair of numbers with the two dice can be computed by multiplying the probability

Table 4.3 Outcomes corresponding to (X, Y)

	Y		
X	0	1	2
0	$(2,2), (4,4), (6,6)$	—	$(1,1), (3,3), (5,5)$
1	—	$(1,2), (2,1), (3,2)$ $(2,3), (4,3), (3,4)$ $(5,4), (4,5), (6,5)$ $(5,6)$	—
2	$(2,4), (4,2), (6,4)$ $(4,6)$	—	$(1,3), (3,1), (5,3)$ $(3,5)$
3	—	$(2,5), (5,2), (6,3)$ $(3,6), (1,4), (4,1)$	—
4	$(6,2), (2,6)$	—	$(1,5), (5,1)$
5	—	$(1,6), (6,1)$	—

of the first number on the first die with the probability of the second number on the second die. These concepts will be discussed in more detail later in this chapter but it is instructive to consider an example of dependent random variables.

Consider a new example in which X is defined as the absolute difference in the scores on two dice and Y is the number of dice with an odd score when two dice are thrown. The possible outcomes corresponding to this experiment are provided in Table 4.3.

Corresponding to this table of outcomes it is straightforward to tabulate the joint probability associated with each pair of x and y values. This is shown in Table 4.4.

Table 4.4 Relative frequency of outcomes $f(x, y)$

	Y			
X	0	1	2	$f_X(x)$
0	$\frac{3}{36}$	0	$\frac{3}{36}$	$\frac{6}{36}$
1	0	$\frac{10}{36}$	0	$\frac{10}{36}$
2	$\frac{4}{36}$	0	$\frac{4}{36}$	$\frac{8}{36}$
3	0	$\frac{6}{36}$	0	$\frac{6}{36}$
4	$\frac{2}{36}$	0	$\frac{2}{36}$	$\frac{4}{36}$
5	0	$\frac{2}{36}$	0	$\frac{2}{36}$
$f_Y(y)$	$\frac{9}{36}$	$\frac{18}{36}$	$\frac{9}{36}$	

As in our previous example the marginal distribution associated with random variables is found by summing the probabilities for each value of the random variable irrespective of the value taken by the second random variable. In the case in Table 4.4 the marginal probability function for x is given by summing across the rows of the table and the marginal probability function for y is given by summing down the columns of the table.

Looking at the values of $f(x,y)$, $f(x)$ and $f(y)$ in Table 4.4, it can be seen that

$$f(x,y) \neq f(x)f(y)$$

for any two values of x and y. For example, $f(X = 1) = \frac{1}{36}$, $f(Y = 1) = \frac{1}{36}$ (from Table 4.2) but $f(X = 1, Y = 1) = \frac{3}{36}$ from Table 4.4. Therefore we can deduce that the random variables X and Y are *dependent*. This is true in the sense that the probability of the occurrence of a specific value of X is not invariant to what value Y may take. In this example a moment's thought should convince you that if one of the two dice has an odd score then it is more likely that the absolute difference between the scores on the two dice is 1 rather than 3 or 5.

Being concerned about the likelihood of the values of one random variable given a fixed value of a second random variable leads us to the concept of a *conditional* probability function. Such a conditional probability function of x given y is written as

$$f(x|y)$$

Confining our interest to the situation in which there is one odd scoring die, that is $y = 1$, we may be interested in the relative probabilities associated with x given $y = 1$. Since the total probability that $y = 1$ is 18/36 then any individual cell probability (associated with a unique value of x and y) must be divided by 18/36 to be found in relative terms. We would write this as

$$f(x|y) = \frac{f(x,y)}{f(y)}$$

Hence the conditional probability function of x given $y = 1$ is

x	0	1	2	3	4	5
$f(x\|y = 1)$	0	10/18	0	6/18	0	2/18

So far in this chapter the exposition has described a single example. This was a deliberate attempt to introduce the notion of a bivariate distribution in an informal manner in such a way that it would seem like a logical extension of the concept of a distribution for a single random variable. However, in order to progress further it is necessary to introduce the concepts we need more formally. Indeed, we have in our example, so far, considered only the idea of a bivariate discrete distribution. The remainder of this discussion concerns not only discrete bivariate distributions but also bivariate continuous distributions. Therefore we shall introduce the concepts for both types of distribution in parallel since the conceptual leap from using summation signs in relating to discrete random variables to integrals to relate to continuous random variables was undertaken in the last two chapters.

We shall start by introducing the concepts of bivariate discrete and bivariate continuous joint density functions and go on to consider bivariate cumulative distribution functions and then marginal and conditional density functions in the manner we did with our discrete example above. Once all the necessary concepts have been introduced we will describe two examples: one of a bivariate discrete probability function and the other of a bivariate continuous density function.

Definition 4.2.1 If X and Y are discrete random variables the function given by

$$f(x, y) = P(X = x, Y = y)$$

for each pair of values (x, y) within the range of X and Y is called a *joint probability function* (j.p.f.).

Therefore the joint probability function describes the probability associated with specific values of both X and Y for all possible values that these random variables can take.

Theorem 4.2.1 A bivariate function is a joint probability function for random variables X and Y iff
(a) $f(x, y) \geqslant 0$ for each pair of (x, y) within its domain. The function f is non-negative for any pair of values of X and Y.
(b) $\Sigma_x \Sigma_y f(x, y) = 1$ where the summation extends over all possible pairs (x, y) within its domain; i.e. the total probability associated with all values of the random variables X and Y over their ranges is 1.

Definition 4.2.2 If X and Y are discrete random variables the function given by

$$F(a, b) = P\{X \leqslant a, Y \leqslant b\} = \sum_{x \leqslant a} \sum_{y \leqslant b} f(x, y) \qquad \text{for } -\infty < x, y < \infty$$

is the *joint cumulative distribution function* of X and Y.

This function therefore describes the probability that X is less than or equal to a *and* Y is less than or equal to b for all possible values of a and b.

Definition 4.2.3 If X and Y are continuous random variables then a function $f(x, y)$ is called a *joint probability density function* (j.p.d.f.) iff

$$P\{(X, Y) \in C\} = \iint\limits_{(x,y) \in C} f(x, y) \, dx \, dy$$

for any region C in the xy plane.

Therefore a joint probability density function describes the probability associated with a range of values of X and Y for any possible region C.

Theorem 4.2.2 A function is a joint probability function of continuous random variables X and Y iff

(a) $f(x, y) \geq 0$ for $-\infty < x, y < \infty$

(b) $\displaystyle\int_{-\infty}^{\infty}\int_{-\infty}^{\infty} f(x, y) \, dx \, dy = 1$

This result is directly analogous to Theorem 4.2.1 for discrete random variables. It requires the density to be non-negative and have the property that when integrated the probability sums to 1.

Definition 4.2.4 If X and Y are continuous random variables then the *joint cumulative distribution function* (j.c.d.f.) is given by

$$F(a, b) = P\{X \in (-\infty, a), Y \in (-\infty, b)\}$$
$$= \int_{-\infty}^{b}\int_{-\infty}^{b} f(x, y) \, dx \, dy$$

A joint cumulative distribution function is a function that specifies the probability associated with X being less than or equal to some value a and Y being less than or equal to some value b for all possible values of a and b.

Notice that it follows from Definition 4.2.3 that the relation between the joint probability function and the joint cumulative distribution function is

$$f(a, b) = \frac{\partial^2 F(a, b)}{\partial a \, \partial b}$$

wherever the partial derivatives are defined. Therefore the joint density can be obtained by partially differentiating the distribution function with respect to both random variables.

Definition 4.2.5 Given the joint probability function $f(x, y)$, the *marginal probability density function of x* (m.p.d.f.) is

$$f_X(x) = \int_{-\infty}^{\infty} f(x, y)\, dy \qquad -\infty < x < \infty$$

Likewise the marginal probability density function of y is

$$f_Y(y) = \int_{-\infty}^{\infty} f(x, y)\, dx \qquad -\infty < y < \infty$$

Note that:

1. The marginal probability density function of a discrete random variable X can also be obtained from the relevant joint probability function by summing (rather than integrating) over the range of values of Y (provided Y is also discrete).
2. It is not possible to infer a unique joint probability density function from the marginal probability density functions. This is because a given pair of marginal probability density functions of X and Y could give rise to many possible joint densities over X and Y.

3. $\dfrac{\partial(F_X(x))}{\partial x} = f_X(x) \qquad \dfrac{\partial(F_Y(y))}{\partial y} = f_Y(y)$

Therefore the marginal densities are related to the marginal cumulative distribution functions in the standard way; the former is the partial derivative of the latter with respect to the appropriate random variable.

Definition 4.2.6 If $f(x, y)$ is the joint probability density function of continuous random variables X and Y then the *conditional probability density function of X given that $Y = y$*, the cumulative probability density function, is defined for all values of y such that $f_Y(y) > 0$, by

$$f_{X|Y}(x|y) = \frac{f(x, y)}{f_Y(y)}$$

Note that a conditional probability density function is also a conventional probability density function with the appropriate properties (see Theorem 4.2.2).

Definition 4.2.7 The *conditional cumulative distribution function of X given $Y = y$* (c.c.d.f.) is

$$F_{X|Y}(a|y) = P\{X \leqslant a | Y = y\} = \int_{-\infty}^{a} f_{X|Y}(x|y)\, dx$$

In Chapter 1 the notion of independent events was introduced. It is possible to define independent random variables analogously.

Definition 4.2.8 The random variables X and Y are said to be *independent* iff

$$f(x,y) = f_X(x)f_Y(y) \qquad \text{for all } x,y$$

Thus, intuitively, X and Y are independent if knowing the value of one does not change the distribution of the other. Random variables that are not independent are said to be *dependent*.

Proposition 4.2.3 If random variables X, Y are independent,

$$f_{X|Y}(x|y) = f_X(x)$$

PROOF Using Definition 4.2.8,

$$f_{X|Y}(x|y) = \frac{f(x,y)}{f_Y(y)}$$
$$= \frac{f_X(x)f_Y(y)}{f_Y(y)}$$
$$= f_X(x)$$

Example 4.2.1 Consider the discrete random variables X and Y which can take only values 1, 2 and 3 and 1, 2, 3 and 4 respectively. Let their joint probability function be

	Y			
X	1	2	3	4
1	.1	0	.1	0
2	.3	0	.1	.2
3	0	.2	0	0

Evaluate $P(1 < X \leq 3, 2 \leq Y \leq 3)$.

$$P(1 < X \leq 3, 2 \leq Y \leq 3) = \sum_{X=2}^{3} \sum_{Y=2}^{3} f(x,y)$$
$$= f(2,2) + f(2,3) + f(3,2) + f(3,3)$$
$$= 0 + .1 + .2 + 0$$
$$= .3$$

Evaluate the joint cumulative distribution function associated with X and Y.

X	$1 > y$	$1 \leqslant y < 2$	$2 \leqslant y < 3$	$3 \leqslant y < 4$	$y \geqslant 4$
			Y		
$1 > x$	0	0	0	0	0
$1 \leqslant x < 2$	0	.1	.1	.2	.2
$2 \leqslant x < 3$	0	.4	.4	.6	.8
$x \geqslant 3$	0	.4	.6	.8	1

The marginal probability function of X is

X	1	2	3
$f_X(x)$	0.2	0.6	0.2

The marginal probability function of Y is

Y	1	2	3	4
$f_Y(y)$	0.4	0.2	0.2	0.2

The conditional probability function of Y given $X = 2$ is

Y	1	2	3	4
$P(Y \mid X = 2)$	$\frac{1}{2}$	0	$\frac{1}{6}$	$\frac{1}{3}$

X and Y are dependent (i.e. not independent) because $P(X, Y) \neq P(X)P(Y)$ for all X and Y. For example, $P(X = 2, Y = 2) = 0 \neq P(X = 2)P(Y = 2) = .6(.2)$.

Example 4.2.2 Assume that the joint probability density function of two continuous random variables X and Y is

$$f(x,y) = \begin{cases} c(x+2y) & \text{for } 0 < x < 1, 0 < y < 1 \\ 0 & \text{elsewhere} \end{cases}$$

This example forms the basis of Program 30.

Evaluate c. Since f is a joint probability density function then

$$\int_0^1 \int_0^1 c(x+2y)\,dx\,dy = 1$$

$$= c \int_0^1 \left[\frac{x^2}{2} + 2yx\right]_0^1 dy = c\left[\frac{y}{2} + y^2\right]_0^1$$

$$\Rightarrow c = \tfrac{2}{3}$$

Find the marginal probability density functions of X and Y:

$$f_X(x) = \int_{-\infty}^{\infty} f(x,y)\,dy = \int_0^1 \tfrac{2}{3}(x+2y)\,dy = \begin{cases} \tfrac{2}{3}(x+1) & 0 < x < 1 \\ 0 & \text{elsewhere} \end{cases}$$

$$f_Y(y) = \int_{-\infty}^{\infty} f(x,y)\,dy = \int_0^1 \tfrac{2}{3}(x+2y)\,dx = \begin{cases} \tfrac{1}{3}(1+4y) & 0 < y < 1 \\ 0 & \text{elsewhere} \end{cases}$$

Find the conditional density of X given Y:

$$f(x|y) = \frac{f(x,y)}{f_Y(y)} = \frac{\tfrac{2}{3}(x+2y)}{\tfrac{1}{3}(1+4y)}$$

$$= \begin{cases} \dfrac{2x+4y}{1+4y} & 0 < x < 1 \\ 0 & \text{elsewhere} \end{cases}$$

Evaluate $P(X \le \tfrac{1}{2}|Y = \tfrac{1}{2})$:

$$f_X(x|Y = \tfrac{1}{2}) = \frac{2x+4y}{1+4y} = \frac{2x+2}{3}$$

$$P(X \le \tfrac{1}{2}|Y = \tfrac{1}{2}) = \int_0^{1/2} \frac{2x+2}{3}\,dx = \tfrac{5}{12}$$

Evaluate $P(0 < X < \tfrac{1}{2}, \tfrac{1}{2} < Y < 1)$:

$$\int_{1/2}^1 \int_0^{1/2} \tfrac{2}{3}(x+2y)\,dx\,dy = \tfrac{2}{3}\int_{1/2}^1 \left[\frac{x^2}{2} + 2yx\right]_0^{1/2} dy$$

$$= \tfrac{2}{3}\int_{1/2}^1 (\tfrac{1}{8} + y)\,dy = \tfrac{2}{3}\left[\tfrac{1}{8}y + \frac{y^2}{2}\right]_{1/2}^1$$

$$= \tfrac{2}{3}[(\tfrac{1}{8} + \tfrac{1}{2}) - (\tfrac{1}{16} + \tfrac{1}{8})] = \tfrac{2}{3} \times \tfrac{7}{16} = \tfrac{7}{24}$$

Find the joint cumulative distribution function of X and Y.

For $0 < x, y < 1$:

$$F(a, b) = \int_0^b \int_0^a \tfrac{2}{3}(x + 2y)\,dx\,dy$$

$$= \tfrac{2}{3} \int_0^b \left[\frac{x^2}{2} + 2yx \right]_0^a dy = \tfrac{2}{3} \int_0^b \frac{a^2}{2} + 2ya\,dy$$

$$= \tfrac{2}{3} \left[\frac{a^2 y}{2} + y^2 a \right]_0^b = \tfrac{2}{3} \left(\frac{a^2 b}{2} + b^2 a \right)$$

For $x \geqslant 1, 0 < y < 1$:

$$F(a, b) = \int_0^y \int_0^1 \tfrac{2}{3}(x + 2y)\,dx\,dy$$

$$= \tfrac{2}{3} \left[\frac{y}{2} + y^2 \right]_0^y$$

$$= \tfrac{2}{3} \left(\frac{y}{2} + y^2 \right)$$

For $0 < x < 1, y \geqslant 1$:

$$F(a, b) = \int_0^1 \int_0^x \tfrac{2}{3}(x + 2y)\,dx\,dy$$

$$= \tfrac{2}{3} \left[\frac{x^2 y}{2} + y^2 x \right]_0^1$$

$$= \tfrac{2}{3} \left(\frac{x^2}{2} + x \right)$$

Therefore,

$$F(x, y) = \begin{cases} 0 & x \leqslant 0, y \leqslant 0 \\ 0 & x \leqslant 0, y > 0 \\ 0 & x > 0, y \leqslant 0 \\ \tfrac{2}{3} \left(\dfrac{y}{2} + y^2 \right) & x \geqslant 1, 0 < y < 1 \\ \tfrac{2}{3} \left(\dfrac{x^2}{2} + x \right) & 0 < x < 1, y \geqslant 1 \\ \tfrac{2}{3} \left(\dfrac{x^2 y}{2} + y^2 x \right) & 0 < x < 1, 0 < y < 1 \\ 1 & x \geqslant 1, y \geqslant 1 \end{cases}$$

The density function is drawn in Fig. 4.1 and an explanation is given below.

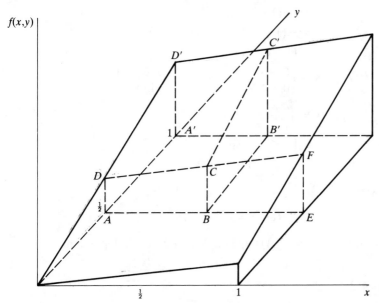

Figure 4.1

In terms of the diagram,

$P(0 < X < \frac{1}{2}, \frac{1}{2} < Y < 1) =$ volume of block $ABCDA'B'C'D'$ as a proportion of 1. Also,

$$P(X \le \tfrac{1}{2} | Y = \tfrac{1}{2}) = \frac{\text{area ABCD}}{\text{area AEFD}}$$

Notice again that X and Y are dependent since

$$f_X(x)f(y) \ne f(x, y)$$
$$\tfrac{2}{9}(x + 1)(1 + 4y) \ne \tfrac{2}{3}(x + 2y)$$

Example 4.2.3 Given the joint probability density function

$$f(x, y) = \begin{cases} e^{-x}e^{-y} & \text{for } x > 0, y > 0 \\ 0 & \text{elsewhere} \end{cases}$$

find the joint cumulative distribution function of X and Y. Are X and Y independent?

$$F(x, y) = \int_0^x \int_0^y e^{-a}e^{-b} \, da \, db$$

$$= \int_0^y \left[-e^{-a}e^{-b} \right]_0^x db = \int_0^y \left[1 - e^{-x} \right] e^{-b} \, db$$

$$= [-(1 - e^{-x})e^{-b}]_0^y$$
$$= -(1 - e^{-x})e^{-y} + (1 - e^{-x})$$
$$= (1 - e^{-x})(1 - e^{-y})$$

$$F(x,y) = \begin{cases} (1 - e^{-x})(1 - e^{-y}) & x \geqslant 0, \, y \geqslant 0 \\ 0 & \text{elsewhere} \end{cases}$$

$$f_X(x) = \int_0^\infty e^{-x} e^{-y} \, dy$$
$$= [-e^{-x} e^{-y}]_0^\infty$$
$$= e^{-x} \qquad \text{for } x > 0$$

Likewise

$$f_Y(y) = e^{-y} \qquad \text{for } y > 0$$

Therefore $f(x,y) = f(x)f(y)$ and X and Y are independent.

Exercises 4.2

Exercise 4.2.1 Suppose the joint probability distribution of X and Y is represented by the following table:

	Z		
X	2	4	6
3	.2	0	.2
4	0	.2	0
5	.2	0	.2

(a) Are X and Z independent? Explain.
(b) Find the marginal distributions of X and Z.
(c) Find the conditional distribution of Z given that $X = 3$.

Exercise 4.2.2 For the probability distribution tabulated in Exercise 4.2.1, leaving the entries in the first row the same, change the entries in the other two rows so that X and Z are independent.

Exercise 4.2.3 The random variables X, Y are independent and have the following distributions:

j	2	3	4
$P(X = j)$	$\frac{1}{2}$	$\frac{1}{4}$	$\frac{1}{4}$

k	1	2
$P(Y = k)$	$\frac{2}{3}$	$\frac{1}{3}$

Let $U = X + Y$ and $V = X/Y$. What pairs of values can U and V take? Obtain the joint distribution of U and V, the marginal distribution of V and the conditional distribution of U given that $V = 2$.

Exercise 4.2.4 The joint probability function of two discrete random variables X and Y is given by

$$f(x,y) = \begin{cases} c[(x-2)+y] & \text{for } 2 \leq x \leq 4, 0 \leq y \leq 3 \\ 0 & \text{otherwise} \end{cases}$$

where x and y can take only integer values.
   (a) Find c.
   (b) Find $P(X = 4, Y = 1)$.
   (c) Find $P(X \geq 3, Y \leq 1)$.
   (d) Find the marginal probability function of Y.
   (e) Find the conditional density of Y given $X = 4$. Evaluate $P(Y = 3 \mid X = 4)$.
   (f) Are X and Y independent?

Exercise 4.2.5 Consider the experiment of rolling a fair die and dealing a poker hand of five cards from a pack of playing cards. Let X be the number on the die and Y be the number of hearts in the poker hand. Find the joint probability function of X and Y.

Exercise 4.2.6 A pair of dice are tossed. Let X be the maximum number on the two dice and Y be the absolute difference between the scores on the two dice.
   (a) Find the joint probability function of X and Y.
   (b) Find the functional form of the marginal probability function of X.
   (c) Find the conditional probability function of Y given $X = 4$.
   (d) Evaluate $P(X \leq 5)$, $P(3 \leq X \leq 4, 2 \leq Y \leq 3)$, $P(3 < Y < 7)$, $P(Y \leq 1 \mid X = 3)$.
   (e) Are X and Y independent?

Exercise 4.2.7 Suppose X and Y are continuous random variables with the following joint probability density function:

$$f(x,y) = \begin{cases} k(x+y) & \text{for } 0 \leqslant x \leqslant 1, 0 \leqslant y \leqslant 2 \\ 0 & \text{otherwise} \end{cases}$$

(a) Find k. Are X and Y independent?
(b) Find $P(0 \leqslant X \leqslant \frac{1}{2}, 0 \leqslant Y \leqslant 1)$.
(c) Find the marginal densities of X and Y.
(d) Find the conditional density of X given $Y = \frac{1}{2}$.

Exercise 4.2.8 Answer Exercise 4.2.4 if $f(x,y)$ is defined as follows:

$$f(x,y) = \begin{cases} k(1-x)(2-y) & \text{for } 0 \leqslant x \leqslant 1, 0 \leqslant y \leqslant 2 \\ 0 & \text{otherwise} \end{cases}$$

Exercise 4.2.9 Let X and Y be continuous variates with joint probability density function

$$f(x,y) = \begin{cases} k(x^2 + 2xy) & \text{for } 0 < x < 1 \text{ and } 0 < y < 1 \\ 0 & \text{otherwise} \end{cases}$$

(a) Evaluate the normalizing constant k.
(b) Find the joint cumulative distribution of X and Y and the marginal probability density function of X.
(c) Compute the probability of the event '$X \leqslant Y$'.

Exercise 4.2.10 Let X and Y be continuous variates with joint cumulative distribution function

$$F(x,y) = kxy(x+y) \qquad \text{for } 0 < x < 1 \text{ and } 0 < y < 1$$

(a) Evaluate the constant k and find the joint probability density function of X and Y.
(b) Find the marginal and conditional probability density functions of X.
(c) Evaluate the following:

$$P(X < .5, Y < .5) \qquad P(X < .5) \qquad P(X < .5 \mid Y < .5)$$

Exercise 4.2.11 Let X and Y be continuous variates with joint probability density function

$$f(x,y) = kx(x+y) \qquad \text{for } 0 < x < 1 \text{ and } 0 < y < 1$$

Evaluate k and find the marginal probability density functions of X and Y.

Exercise 4.2.12 Let $F(x,y)$ be the distribution function of X and Y. Show that

$$P(a < X \leqslant b, c < Y \leqslant d) = F(b,d) - F(b,c) - F(a,d) + F(a,c)$$

for all real constants $a < b$, $c < d$.

Exercise 4.2.13 Two adjacent areas of London have an incidence of V-1 hits that are independent and Poisson distributed with parameters λ_1 and λ_2 respectively. It is reported that the total number of V-1 hits in these areas is 15. What is the conditional distribution of hits in area 1?

*4.3 THE BIVARIATE NORMAL DISTRIBUTION

One of the most important bivariate continuous distributions is the bivariate normal distribution. This distribution has many useful applications. There are numerous applications of measurements that have been assumed to be bivariate normal; e.g. the height and I.Q. of individuals in a population, the score of two separate examinations for a set of examinees, the coordinates of the position of a shot at a target. (Indeed the last example is the assumption that underlies Program 18.) There are many other examples and one may appeal to the same process of the central limit theorem in the single-variable case (discussed in Section 3.6) to suggest that the bivariate normal is a common occurrence in jointly distributed random variables. The bivariate normal distribution has a characteristic 'hill' shape, the exact form of which depends on its parameters. At this point it is important to define this distribution more formally by writing out its density function. The bivariate normal has the density $f(x,y)$ where X and Y are continuous variates with joint probability density function

$$f(x,y) = \frac{1}{2\pi\sigma_y\sigma_x\sqrt{1-\varrho^2}}\exp\left\{-\frac{1}{2(1-\varrho^2)^2}\left[\left(\frac{x-\mu_x}{\sigma_x}\right)^2 + \left(\frac{y-\mu_y}{\sigma_y}\right)^2\right.\right.$$

$$\left.\left. -2\varrho\frac{(x-\mu_x)(y-\mu_y)}{\sigma_x\sigma_y}\right]\right\}$$

for $-\infty < x < \infty$ and $-\infty < y < \infty$, where ϱ is a constant and $-1 < \varrho < 1$.

The parameters μ_x and μ_y correspond to the means of x and y respectively, σ_x and σ_y to the standard deviation of x and y respectively and ϱ to the correlation coefficient. These concepts were introduced in a descriptive context in Book 1. A more formal presentation of expectation is provided in Chapter 5 of the present volume.

The random variables X and Y are said to be jointly normally distributed random variables and their joint distribution is said to be bivariate normal if it has the joint density given above. The bivariate normal distribution has many important properties, several of which are summarized in Theorem 4.3.1.

Theorem 4.3.1[†] If (X, Y) have a bivariate normal distribution with parameters μ_x, μ_y, σ_x, σ_y and ϱ, then

(a) X is a normal random variable with parameters μ_x and σ_x and Y is a normal random variable with parameters μ_y and σ_y.

(b) X and Y are independent if and only if $\varrho = 0$.

(c) The conditional distribution for Y given $X = x$ is normal with mean $\mu_y + \varrho(\sigma_y/\sigma_x)(x - \mu_x)$ and variance $\sigma_y^2(1 - \sigma^2)$.

These results suggest that it can be shown that if X and Y are normal random variables with means equal to μ_x and μ_y respectively and standard deviations σ_x and σ_y, it can also be shown that x and y are independent if and only if the correlation coefficient between x and y, ϱ, is equal to zero.

The shape and form of the bivariate normal distribution depends on the values of its parameters. Two examples of the shape of this density are illustrated in the isometric 'mesh plots' drawn in Figs. 4.2a and b and 4.3a and b. These diagrams may be drawn on your computer by using Program 34. For the plots in Fig. 4.2 the variables X and Y are independent with $\varrho = 0$, and $\sigma_x = \sigma_y$. The plots in Fig. 4.3a and b have $\varrho \neq 0$ and $\sigma_x \neq \sigma_y$.

At this point the reader is invited to use the program to explore the shape that this distribution takes for different values of its parameters.

Exercises 4.3

Exercise 4.3.1 Using Program 33 where μ_x and μ_y are fixed, put in the following values of the other parameters to observe the shape of the mesh plot produced:

(a) $\sigma_x = 1$, $\sigma_y = 1$, $\varrho = 0$

(b) $\sigma_x = 2$, $\sigma_y = 2$, $\varrho = 0$

(c) $\sigma_x = .5$, $\sigma_y = .5$, $\varrho = 0$

(d) $\sigma_x = 1$, $\sigma_y = 1$, $\varrho = .5$

(e) $\sigma_x = 1$, $\sigma_y = 1$, $\varrho = .98$

(f) $\sigma_x = .5$, $\sigma_y = .5$, $\varrho = .98$

(g) $\sigma_x = 1$, $\sigma_y = 1$, $\varrho = -.98$

(h) $\sigma_x = .5$, $\sigma_y = 2$, $\varrho = 0$

(i) $\sigma_x = .5$, $\sigma_y = 2$, $\varrho = .8$

(j) $\sigma_x = 2$, $\sigma_y = .5$, $\varrho = .2$

Exercise 4.3.2 What happens in the bivariate normal if $\varrho = 1$?

In general you should observe:

(a) The 'spread' of the distribution getting larger in both the x and y directions as σ_x and σ_y increase.

---

† Proof of this result can be found in Larson (1982, p. 309) or De Groot (1975, pp. 248–251).

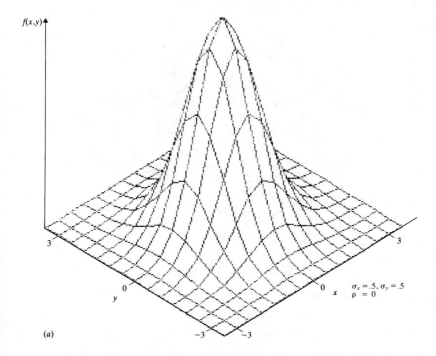

$f(x,y)$

y

x

$\sigma_x = .5, \sigma_y = .5$
$\rho = 0$

3

3

0

0

−3

−3

(a)

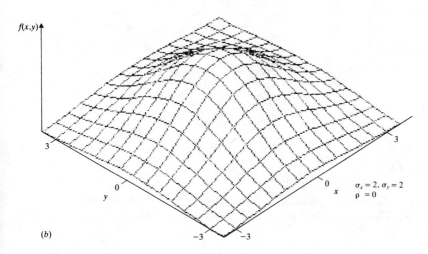

$f(x,y)$

y

x

$\sigma_x = 2, \sigma_y = 2$
$\rho = 0$

3

3

0

0

−3

−3

(b)

Figure 4.2

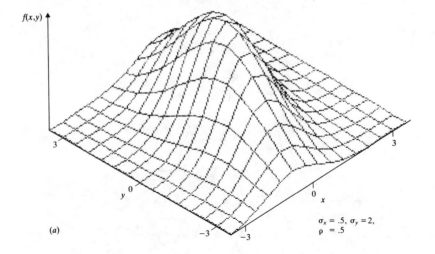

$$\sigma_x = .5,\ \sigma_y = 2,$$
$$\rho = .5$$

(a)

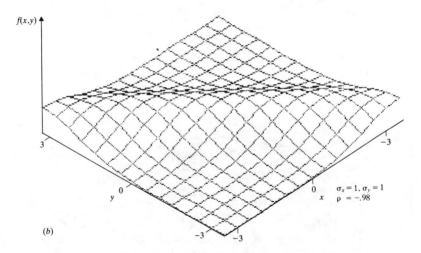

$$\sigma_x = 1,\ \sigma_y = 1$$
$$\rho = -.98$$

(b)

Figure 4.3

(b) A circular, symmetric 'bell shape' is found when $\varrho = 0$.
(c) The 'tightening' of the distribution to a ridge as ϱ increases.

*4.4 DISTRIBUTIONS OF FUNCTIONS OF RANDOM VARIABLES

Given a set of random variables $X_1, \ldots, X_n$ and their joint probability density function (j.p.d.f.) or their joint cumulative distribution function, we are often interested in finding the probability density function of some new random variables $Y_1, Y_2, \ldots, Y_n$ which are functions of the original random variables. The probability density function of any given $y = g(x)$ or any joint probability density function of $y_1, \ldots, y_m$ where $y_1 = g_1(x_1, \ldots, x_n) \ldots y_m = g_m(x_1, \ldots, x_n)$ can be calculated using the appropriate techniques.

There are several methods of doing this but we shall discuss only two: the distribution function technique and the more general transformation technique. Also we will be concerned only with, at most, bivariate distributions and leave aside the distributions of functions of multivariate random variables.

Distribution function technique

A straightforward method of obtaining the probability density of a function of continuous random variables consists of first finding its distribution function and then its density by differentiation. Thus, if $X_1, X_2, \ldots, X_n$ are continuous random variables with a given joint probability density, the probability density of $Y = f_Y(X_1, X_2, \ldots, X_n)$ is obtained by first determining an expression for the probabilities

$$F_Y(y) = P(Y \leqslant y) = P[g(X_1, X_2, \ldots, X_n) \leqslant y]$$

and then differentiating to get

$$f(y) = \frac{\mathrm{d}F_Y(y)}{\mathrm{d}y}$$

Example 4.4.1 If the probability density of x is given by

$$f(x) = \begin{cases} 6x(1-x) & \text{for } 0 < x < 1 \\ 0 & \text{elsewhere} \end{cases}$$

find the probability density of $Y = X^3$.

Letting $F_Y(y)$ denote the value of the distribution function of Y at y, we can write

$$\begin{aligned} F_Y(y) &= P(Y \leqslant y) \\ &= P(X^3 \leqslant y) \\ &= P(X \leqslant y^{1/3}) \\ &= \int_0^{y^{1/3}} 6x(1-x)\,\mathrm{d}x \\ &= 3y^{2/3} - 2y \end{aligned}$$

and hence,

$$f_Y(y) = 2(y^{-1/3} - 1) \qquad \text{for } 0 < y < 1$$

Elsewhere $f_Y(y) = 0$.

The transformation technique

The transformation technique involves changing variables in the density function. The idea is best illustrated intuitively by considering a random variable X with a density function $f(x)$. Suppose that a new variable Y is defined by the relation

$$Y = g(X)$$

The variable Y must then also have a density function defined in terms of the density function for X and the relation $Y = g(X)$.

Consider that the relation between Y and X is monotonically increasing as shown in Fig. 4.4.

From Fig. 4.4 any point x' such that $g(x') \leq y'$ is the same as the corresponding point y' such that $x' \leq g^{-1}(y')$. Hence

$$P(Y \leq y) = P(X \leq x)$$

or $$F_Y(y) = F_X(x)$$

Differentiating with respect to y (using the Chain rule):

$$f_Y(y) = \frac{\mathrm{d}F_Y(y)}{\mathrm{d}y} = \frac{\mathrm{d}F_X(x)}{\mathrm{d}x}\frac{\mathrm{d}x}{\mathrm{d}y} = f_X(x)\frac{\mathrm{d}x}{\mathrm{d}y}$$

Therefore

$$f_Y(y) = f_X(x)\frac{\mathrm{d}x}{\mathrm{d}y}$$

If y were a decreasing function of X then $\mathrm{d}x/\mathrm{d}y$ would be negative, thus

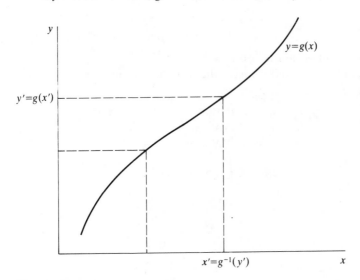

Figure 4.4

giving an impossible negative value for the density function. The absolute value of the derivative must therefore be taken and the result reformulated as

$$f_Y(y) = f_X(x) \left| \frac{dx}{dy} \right|$$

A further practical problem involved in writing out the probability density function for y is that $f(x)$ is written in terms of single y. We must write this function in its inverse form, i.e. in terms of a single value of X, that is $g^{-1}(y)$. Thus the transformation formula becomes

$$f(y) = f[g^{-1}(y)] \left| \frac{dg^{-1}(y)}{dy} \right|$$

The analogous result holds for two random variables.

Consider transforming a joint probability density function of X_1 and X_2 into a joint probability density function of Y_1 and Y_2, where

$$Y_1 = g_1(X_1, X_2), \qquad Y_2 = g_2(X_1, X_2)$$

and g_1 and g_2 are continuous and monotonic.

Provided there exists a well-behaved density function, f, of x_1 and x_2 over a region R in the x_1, x_2 plane then there is a corresponding function over the region R' in the y_1, y_2 plane. Schematically the relation can be seen in Fig. 4.5 where R, the region over which X_1 and X_2 are defined using f, is mapped onto the region R'. The region R' is the area over which the two new variables Y_1 and Y_2 are defined. Therefore the total probability associated with f over R is equivalent to the probability associated with y_1 and y_2 over R' when this relation is transformed, that is

$$\iint_R f_{X_1, X_2}(x_1, x_2)\, dx_1\, dx_2 = \iint_{R'} f_{Y_1, Y_2}(y_1, y_2)\, |\mathbf{J}|\, dy_1\, dy_2$$

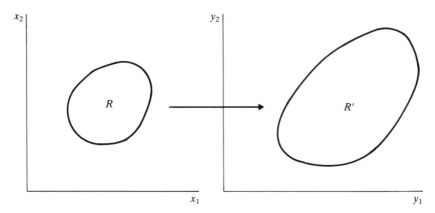

Figure 4.5

where $\mathbf{J}$ is the determinant of the matrix of the first-order partial derivatives:

$$\mathbf{J} = \det \begin{bmatrix} \dfrac{\partial y_1}{\partial x_1} & \dfrac{\partial y_1}{\partial x_2} \\[2ex] \dfrac{\partial y_2}{\partial x_1} & \dfrac{\partial y_2}{\partial x_2} \end{bmatrix}$$

$\mathbf{J}$ is sometimes called the *Jacobian* of the transformation.

Hence the right-hand side of the transformation may be evaluated in terms of y_1 and y_2 by solving the relations g_1 and g_2 in terms of y_1 and y_2 and evaluating the Jacobian. Hence

$$f_{Y_1,Y_2}(y_1,y_2) = f_{X_1,X_2}(x_1,x_2)|\mathbf{J}|^{-1}$$

We may now state these results slightly more formally.

Single variable case Given some random variable X we seek the distribution of $Y = g(X)$ for some $g(.)$.

Theorem 4.4.1 Let X be a continuous random variable having a probability density function f_X. Suppose that $g(x)$ is a strictly increasing or decreasing differentiable[†] (and thus continuous) function of x. Then the random variable Y defined by $Y = g(X)$ has a probability density function given by

$$f_Y(y) = \begin{cases} f_X[g^{-1}(y)]\left|\dfrac{\mathrm{d}}{\mathrm{d}y}g^{-1}(y)\right| & \text{if } y = g(x) \text{ for some } x \\ 0 & \text{if } y \neq g(x) \text{ for all } x \end{cases}$$

where $g^{-1}(y)$ is defined to equal that value of x such that $g(x) = y$.

Example 4.4.2 Given

$$f_X(x) = \begin{cases} 3x^2 & 0 < x < 1 \\ 0 & \text{otherwise} \end{cases}$$

Find the probability density function of $Y = 1 - X^2$

$$g(y) = 1 - x^2 \Rightarrow g^{-1}(x) = (1-y)^{1/2}$$

$$\frac{\mathrm{d}g^{-1}(y)}{\mathrm{d}y} = \tfrac{1}{2}(1-y)^{-1/2}$$

$$f_Y(y) = \tfrac{1}{2}(1-y)^{-1/2}.3(1-y)$$

$$\Rightarrow \begin{cases} \tfrac{3}{2}(1-y)^{1/2} & 0 < y < 1 \\ 0 & \text{otherwise} \end{cases}$$

---

† Formally we require $g(x)$ to be monotonic and differentiable.

Another way to visualize the problem of finding functions of random variables is to use a 'three-quadrant' diagram. Such a diagram is used in Program 31. This diagram can be illustrated with two examples.

Consider the unit exponential distribution

$$f(x) = e^{-x} \quad \text{for } x \geq 0$$

and let us assume we wish to find the density of Y and Z where

$$Y = g(X) = X^2 \qquad Z = h(X) = X^{1/2}$$

Using the technique above we know that

$$g_Y(y) = f_X[g^{-1}(y)] \left| \frac{dg^{-1}(y)}{dy} \right|$$

$$= e^{-x} \frac{1}{2x}$$

$$= \frac{e^{-y^{1/2}}}{2y^{1/2}}$$

and

$$h_Z(z) = f_X[h^{-1}(z)] \left| \frac{dh^{-1}(z)}{dz} \right|$$

$$= 2e^{-x}$$

$$= 2ze^{-z^2}$$

The position is summarized in Figs. 4.6 and 4.7. In these diagrams the functional relation between y and x is drawn in the upper right-hand quadrant. The original unit exponential density of x is drawn (inverted) in the lower right-hand quadrant. The transformed density in y or z is then drawn in the upper left quadrant. (These diagrams are also used in Morgan (1984).)

Notice in these two examples the shape of the relation between the form of $g(y)$ and $h(z)$. More specifically, the weighting induced by $y = x^2$ makes values of the random variable smaller after the transformation. Likewise the relation $z = x^{1/2}$ induces larger values of the corresponding random variable. These transformations induce the shapes of the density on the random variables y and z which are drawn in the upper left quadrant of Figs. 4.6 and 4.7.

The shaded areas in each diagram are equivalent in the sense that the areas have equal probability associated with them. These diagrams therefore clarify the relation between $f(x)$ and the transformed densities $g(y)$ and $h(z)$.

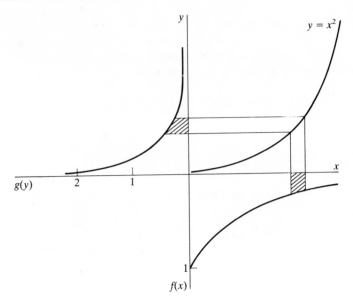

Figure 4.6

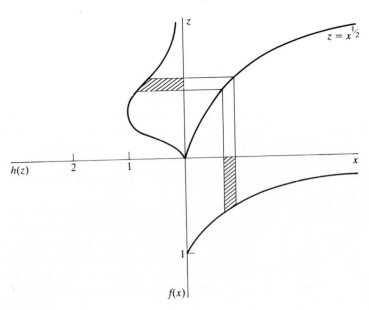

Figure 4.7

Bivariate case

Theorem 4.4.2 Let X_1 and X_2 be jointly continuous random variables with joint probability density function f_{X_1, X_2}. We seek the joint distribution of random variables Y_1 and Y_2 which arise as functions of X_1 and X_2. Let $Y_1 = g_1(X_1, X_2)$ and $Y_2 = g_2(X_1, X_2)$ for some functions g_1 and g_2. Assume for g_1 and g_2 that

(a) $y_1 = g_1(x_1, x_2)$ and $y_2 = g_2(x_1, x_2)$ can be uniquely solved for x_1 and x_2 in terms of y_1 and y_2 with solutions given by $x_1 = h_1(y_1, y_2)$ and $x_2 = h_2(y_1, y_2)$.

(b) The functions g_1 and g_2 have continuous partial derivatives at all points (x_1, x_2) and are such that the determinant

$$
\mathbf{J}(x_1, x_2) = \begin{vmatrix} \dfrac{\partial g_1}{\partial x_1} & \dfrac{\partial g_1}{\partial x_2} \\[2mm] \dfrac{\partial g_2}{\partial x_1} & \dfrac{\partial g_2}{\partial x_2} \end{vmatrix} = \frac{\partial g_1}{\partial x_1}\frac{\partial g_2}{\partial x_2} - \frac{\partial g_1}{\partial x_2}\frac{\partial g_2}{\partial x_1} \neq 0
$$

at all points (x_1, x_2).

Under conditions (a) and (b), Y_1 and Y_2 are jointly continuous with a joint probability density function given by

$$
f_{Y_1, Y_2}(y_1, y_2) = f_{X_1, X_2}(x_1, x_2)|\mathbf{J}(x_1, x_2)|^{-1}
$$

where $x_1 = h_1(y_1, y_2)$, $x_2 = h_2(y_1, y_2)$. Notice that we take the absolute value of the reciprocal of $\mathbf{J}$ to determine f_{Y_1, Y_2}.

Example 4.4.3 Let X_1 and X_2 be continuous random variables with a joint probability density function given by

$$
f_{X_1, X_2}(x_1, x_2) = \begin{cases} 4x_1 x_2 & 0 < x_1, x_2 < 1 \\ 0 & \text{otherwise} \end{cases}
$$

Find the joint probability density function of Y_1 and Y_2 where

$$
Y_1 = X_1 + X_2 \quad \text{and} \quad Y_2 = X_1 - X_2
$$

The area over which these variables are defined is illustrated in Fig. 4.8.

The Jacobian is

$$
\mathbf{J}(x_1, x_2) = \begin{vmatrix} \dfrac{\partial y_1}{\partial x_1} & \dfrac{\partial y_1}{\partial x_2} \\[2mm] \dfrac{\partial y_2}{\partial x_1} & \dfrac{\partial y_2}{\partial x_2} \end{vmatrix} = \begin{vmatrix} 1 & 1 \\ 1 & -1 \end{vmatrix} = -2
$$

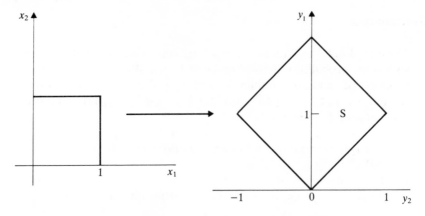

Figure 4.8

Rewriting X_1 and X_2 gives

$$x_1 = \frac{y_1 + y_2}{2} \qquad x_2 = \frac{y_1 - y_2}{2}$$

while

$$f_{Y_1, Y_2}(y_1, y_2) = f_{X_1, X_2}(x_1, x_2)|J|^{-1}$$

gives

$$f_{Y_1, Y_2}(y_1, y_2) = \tfrac{1}{2} \times 4[(\tfrac{1}{2}(y_1 + y_2) \times \tfrac{1}{2}(y_1 - y_2)]$$
$$= \begin{cases} \tfrac{1}{2}(y_1^2 - y_2^2) & y_1, y_2 \in S \\ 0 & \text{otherwise} \end{cases}$$

Example 4.4.4 Let X_1 and X_2 be jointly continuous independent exponential random variables with a joint probability density function

$$f_{X_1, X_2}(x_1, x_2) = \begin{cases} \lambda_1 \lambda_2 e^{-(\lambda_1 x_1 + \lambda_2 x_2)} & x_1 > 0, x_2 > 0 \\ 0 & \text{elsewhere} \end{cases}$$

Find the joint probability density function of Y_1 and Y_2 where $Y_1 = X_1 + X_2$ and $Y_2 = X_1 - X_2$. The area over which these variables are defined is illustrated in Fig. 4.9.

The relevant Jacobian is

$$J(x_1, x_2) = \begin{vmatrix} \dfrac{\partial y_1}{\partial x_1} & \dfrac{\partial y_1}{\partial x_2} \\ \dfrac{\partial y_2}{\partial x_1} & \dfrac{\partial y_2}{\partial x_2} \end{vmatrix} = \begin{vmatrix} 1 & 1 \\ 1 & -1 \end{vmatrix} = -2$$

Rewriting X_1 and X_2 gives

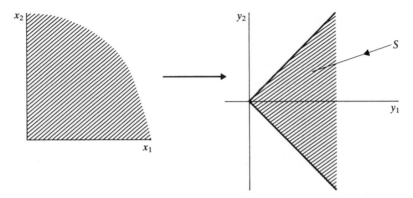

Figure 4.9

$$x_1 = \frac{y + y_2}{2} \qquad x_2 = \frac{y_1 - y_2}{2}$$

Therefore, using

$$f_{Y_1, Y_2}(y_1, y_2) = f_{X_1, X_2}(x_1, x_2)|\mathbf{J}|^{-1}$$

gives

$$f_{Y_1, Y_2}(y_1, y_2) = \begin{cases} \dfrac{\lambda_1 \lambda_2}{2} \exp\left[-\lambda_1\left(\dfrac{y_1 + y_2}{2}\right) - \lambda_2\left(\dfrac{y_1 - y_2}{2}\right) \right] & y_1, y_2 \in S \\ 0 & \text{elsewhere} \end{cases}$$

Exercises 4.4

Exercise 4.4.1 Let the random variable X have the probability function $f(x) = x/10$ for $x = 1, 2, 3, 4$; zero elsewhere. Find the probability function of $Y = 2X - 1$.

Exercise 4.4.2 Let $f(x) = \frac{1}{3}$ for $x = -1, 0, 1$; zero elsewhere, be the probability function of X. Find the probability function of $Y = |X|$.

Exercise 4.4.3 Let the random variable X have a probability density function

$$f(x) = \begin{cases} 2xe^{-x^2} & 0 < X < \infty \\ 0 & \text{elsewhere} \end{cases}$$

Find the probability density function of $Y = X^2$.

Exercise 4.4.4 If $f(x) = 1$, $0 < X < 1$; zero elsewhere, what is the probability density function of X? Find the cumulative distribution function and the probability density function of $Y = X^{1/2}$.

Exercise 4.4.5 For Exercise 4.2.4 define $U = |X - Y|$ and $V = Y + X$. Find the joint probability function of U and V.

Exercise 4.4.6 Given that two random variables U and V have a continuous joint distribution for which the joint probability density function is

$$f(u, v) = \begin{cases} 4uv & 0 < u, v < 1 \\ 0 & \text{otherwise} \end{cases}$$

find the joint probability density function of two new random variables X and Y which are defined by the relations $X = U + V$ and $Y = U - V$.

Exercise 4.4.7 Given that two independent random variables X_1 and X_2 have a continuous joint distribution for which the joint probability density function is

$$f(x_1)f(x_2) = \begin{cases} \frac{1}{4}\exp[(-x_1 + x_2)/2] & 0 < x_1, x_2 < \infty \\ 0 & \text{otherwise} \end{cases}$$

find the joint probability density function of two new random variables Y_1 and Y_2 where

$$Y_1 = \tfrac{1}{2}(X_1 - X_2) \quad \text{and} \quad Y_2 = X_2$$

Exercise 4.4.8 Given that two random variables X_1 and X_2 have a continuous joint distribution for which the joint probability density function is

$$f(x_1, x_2) = \begin{cases} 4x_1x_2 & 0 < x_1 < 1, 0 < x_2 < 1 \\ 0 & \text{otherwise} \end{cases}$$

find the joint probability density function of two new random variables Y_1 and Y_2 which are defined by the relations

$$Y_1 = \frac{X_1}{X_2} \quad Y_2 = X_1X_2$$

Exercise 4.4.9 Let X and Y be independent variates, each having a unit exponential distribution (that is $\lambda = 1$ in Definition 3.7.1). Find the joint distribution of their sum $X + Y$ and their ratio X/Y.

Exercise 4.4.10 Suppose X_1 and X_2 are independent random variables, each uniformly distributed over the interval $(0, 1)$. Let

$$Y_1 = X_1 + X_2 \quad \text{and} \quad Y_2 = X_2 - X_1$$

be two new random variables. Find the joint probability density function of the two new random variables.

FIVE

EXPECTATION

5.1 INTRODUCTION

The first volume of this text on descriptive statistics related to summarizing data. In this context we discussed measures of central tendency and dispersion; more specifically we introduced the mean and variance (and standard deviation) as measures of these data features for use with any empirical set of observations.

In the past three chapters we have described theoretical probability models for use in modelling real empirical data. If the theoretical models to be used are an accurate representation of these empirical data we would expect the theoretical and empirical distributions to be approximately equivalent. A consequence of this equivalence would be that the mean and the variance of the theoretical model would be similar to those to be found in the empirical data. Hence the descriptive statistics to be calculated in summarising data may often need to be compared directly with the properties of the theoretical probability models.

The theoretical analogues of the mean and variance are examples of *moments*. In this chapter we introduce and discuss the moments associated with the probability distributions studied in Chapters 2 and 3.

This chapter will characterize the general nature of the expectation of a random variable and its form for specific examples. In addition we seek to examine higher moments of discrete and continuous distributions and univariate and bivariate distributions and analyze their properties. This will include deriving the mean and variance as examples of expected values or moments of each distribution.

Originally the concept of a *mathematical expectation* arose in connection with games of chance. In simplest terms a lottery must be evaluated in terms of a weighted average formed by multiplying the chances of winning various prizes by the size of the respective prizes. This calculation would determine the breakeven level of the original wager and therefore act as an objective criterion as to whether the bet should be accepted in the first place.

5.2 THE EXPECTATION OF A RANDOM VARIABLE

One of the most important concepts in probability and statistics is the expectation of a random variable. This concept is described in this section and explored in Program 32. It is therefore appropriate to begin by defining this concept.

Definition 5.2.1 If X is a discrete random variable with a probability function $p(x)$ then the *expectation* or expected value of X, denoted by $E[X]$, is

$$E[X] = \sum_x xp(x)$$

The expectation of a random variable X is therefore the weighted average of the possible values of X where the weights are provided by the probability of the associated x value. The expectation of a random variable is commonly referred to as the *mean* or the *first moment*.

The term 'first moment' derives from mechanics in which the problem of the point of balance or centre of gravity of an object is often of interest. This analogy provides a useful picture of the notion of an expected value. If we consider any distribution to be the distribution of weight on a seesaw, then finding the point of balance of that seesaw is equivalent to finding the expectation of that distribution. For example, the point of balance in the distribution in Fig. 5.1 is indicated by the small triangle.

In the calculation of a centre of gravity the contribution of each rectangle in the histogram (distribution) must be judged by weighting its size with its distance from the point of pivot. This is directly analogous to the weighting of the probability of each possible value by its size.

This analogy from mechanics is a useful visual representation of the expected value. More often statisticians wish to think of the expected value as the average value or mean. This is one important measure of 'central

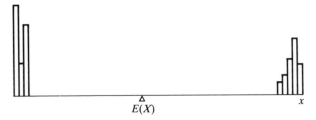

$E(X)$ x

Figure 5.1

tendency' in a distribution which tells us something about its centre (but nothing about its spread).

Example 5.2.1 What is $E[X]$ where X is the number on the roll of one fair die?

$$E[X] = 1(\tfrac{1}{6}) + 2(\tfrac{1}{6}) + 3(\tfrac{1}{6}) + 4(\tfrac{1}{6}) + 5(\tfrac{1}{6})3 + 6(\tfrac{1}{6})$$
$$= \tfrac{7}{2}$$

In this example the expected value of X can be interpreted as the 'average' value that would occur if the die were rolled an infinite number of times.

In the case of a discrete distribution the expectation was found by weighting each value that random variable can take by its associated probability. This was calculated by multiplying each value of x by $f(x)$. In the case of a continuous distribution this could not be done since x takes an infinite number of values. Therefore to compute the expected value of a continuous random variable we must integrate the density function multiplied by x over the whole range of values that x may take. Accordingly the formal definition of expectation for a continuous random variable is:

Definition 5.2.2 If X is a continuous random variable with a probability density function $f(x)$ then the expectation of X is

$$E[X] = \int_{-\infty}^{\infty} x f(x)\, dx$$

(This integral converges if and only if $\int_{-\infty}^{\infty} |x| f(x)\, dx$ is finite.)

Often we are concerned with not only the expectation of a random variable X but also with the expected values of random variables related to X. More specifically we may be interested in some function of X, for example $g(X)$. The law governing the expectation of a function of a random variable is given by Theorem 5.2.1.

Theorem 5.2.1
(a) If X is a discrete random variable with probability function $p(x)$ then for any real-valued function g the expectation of $g(X)$ is

$$E[g(X)] = \sum_x g(x)p(x)$$

(b) If X is a continuous random variable with probability density function $f(x)$ then for any real-valued function g,

$$E[g(X)] = \int_{-\infty}^{\infty} g(x)f(x)\,dx$$

PROOF The proof of these results is beyond the scope of this text but can be found in more advanced treatments, e.g. Ross (1984, pp. 243–245).

Likewise for the bivariate random variable case we can compute the expected value of a function $g(x, y)$ of random variables x and y.

Corollary 5.2.1
(a) If X and Y are discrete random variables with joint probability function $p(x, y)$ then

$$E[g(X, Y)] = \sum_x \sum_y g(x, y)p(x, y)$$

(b) If X and Y are continuous random variables with joint probability density function $f(x, y)$ then

$$E[g(X, Y)] = \int_{-\infty}^{\infty} \int_{-\infty}^{\infty} g(x, y)f(x, y)\,dx\,dy$$

Example 5.2.2 Given

$$f(x) = \begin{cases} \frac{3}{4}(2x - x^2) & 0 < x < 2 \\ 0 & \text{elsewhere} \end{cases}$$

Find $E(X)$, $E(X^2)$:

$$E(X) = \int_0^2 x\tfrac{3}{4}(2x - x^2)dx = [\tfrac{1}{2}x^3 - \tfrac{3}{16}x^4]_0^2 = 1$$

$$E[X^2] = \int_0^2 x^2\tfrac{3}{4}(2x - x^2)dx = [\tfrac{6}{16}x^4 - \tfrac{3}{20}x^5]_0^2 = 1.2$$

Example 5.2.3 Let Y_1 and Y_2 have the following joint probability density function:

$$f_{Y_1,Y_2}(y_1,y_2) = \begin{cases} 3y_1 & 0 \leqslant y_2 \leqslant y_2 \leqslant 1 \\ 0 & \text{elsewhere} \end{cases}$$

Find $E[Y_1 Y_2]$:

$$E[Y_1 Y_2] = \int_0^1 \int_0^{y_1} y_1 y_2\, 3y_1 \, dy_2 \, dy_1 = \int_0^1 \left[3y_1^2 \left(\frac{y_2^2}{2} \right) \right]_0^{y_1} dy_1$$

$$= \int_0^1 \tfrac{3}{2} y_1^4 \, dy_1 = \tfrac{3}{2} \left[\frac{y_1^5}{5} \right]_0^1 = \tfrac{3}{10}$$

The determination of mathematical expectation can often be simplified by using the following theorems. These general theorems concerning mathematical expectation enable us to calculate expected values from other known or easily computed expectations. The proofs are given for continuous variables but may be verified for discrete variables.

Theorem 5.2.2 If a, b are constants:
(a) $E[a] = a$
(b) $E[aX + b] = aE[X] + b$
(c) $E[X + Y] = E[X] + E[Y]$

PROOF

(a) $$E[a] = \int_{-\infty}^{\infty} (a)f(x) \, dx = a \int_{-\infty}^{\infty} f(x) \, dx = a$$

This result states that the expected value of a non-random constant is equal to that constant.

(b) $$E[aX + b] = \int_{-\infty}^{\infty} (ax + b)f(x) \, dx$$

$$= a \int_{-\infty}^{\infty} xf(x) \, dx + b \int_{-\infty}^{\infty} f(x) \, dx$$

$$= aE[X] + b$$

This second result states that the expected value of a linear function of a random variable X is the same linear function of the expected value.

(c) $$E[X + Y] = \int_{-\infty}^{\infty} \int_{-\infty}^{\infty} (x + y)f(x,y) \, dx \, dy$$

$$= \int_{-\infty}^{\infty} \int_{-\infty}^{\infty} xf(x,y) \, dx \, dy + \int_{-\infty}^{\infty} \int_{-\infty}^{\infty} yf(x,y) \, dx \, dy$$

$$= \int_{-\infty}^{\infty} xf_X(x) \, dx + \int_{-\infty}^{\infty} yf_Y(y) \, dy$$

$$= E[X] + E[Y]$$

The third result states that the expected value of the sum of two random variables is equal to the sum of their respective expected values.

(d) From (c) it follows that

$$E[X_1 + X_2 + \cdots + X_n] = E[X_1] + E[X_2] + \cdots + E[X_n]$$

(e) From (b) and (c) it follows that

$$E[aX_1 + bX_2] = aE[X_1] + bE[X_2]$$

Results (d) and (e) follow as logical corollaries to results (a), (b) and (c).

One particularly important expectation of a function of a random variable is known as the *variance*. The concept of the variance of a distribution should be familiar from the treatment in Book 1 on descriptive statistics. There the variance was described as a weighted sum of squared deviations from the mean, where the weights are the respective probabilities of the possible values of the random variable. In descriptive statistics the variance often provides a summary measure of the variability or 'degree of spread' in a distribution. Here we show that the variance of a random variable is also an example of a function of a random variable. Theorem 5.2.2 is immediately useful in the development of an expression for the variance.

Definition 5.2.3 If X is a random variable, with mean μ, then the *variance* of X denoted by σ^2 or var(X) is defined by

$$\text{var}(X) = E[(X - \mu)^2]$$

An alternative formula for var(X) can be derived:

$$\begin{aligned}
\text{var}(X) &= E[(X - \mu)^2] \\
&= E[X^2 - 2\mu X + \mu^2] \\
&= E[X^2] - E[2\mu X] + E[\mu^2] \\
&= E[X^2] - 2\mu E[X] + \mu^2 \\
&= E[X^2] - \mu^2 \\
\text{var}(X) &= E[X^2] - (E[X])^2
\end{aligned}$$

Example 5.2.4 Calculate var(X) when X is the outcome of tossing a fair die.

From Example 5.2.1, $E[X] = \frac{7}{2}$:

$$E[X^2] = 1^2(\tfrac{1}{6}) + 2^2(\tfrac{1}{6}) + 3^2(\tfrac{1}{6}) + 4^2(\tfrac{1}{6}) - 5^2(\tfrac{1}{6}) + 6^2(\tfrac{1}{6})$$

$$= \tfrac{91}{6}$$

$$\text{var}(X) = \tfrac{91}{6} - (\tfrac{7}{2})^2 = \tfrac{35}{12}$$

Example 5.2.5 Let the random variable X have the density function

$$f(x) = \begin{cases} \frac{1}{2}(x+1) & -1 < x < 1 \\ 0 & \text{elsewhere} \end{cases}$$

Find $E[X]$, var(X):

$$E[X] = \int_{-\infty}^{\infty} x f(x) \, dx = \int_{-1}^{1} x \frac{x+1}{2} \, dx = \frac{1}{3}$$

$$\text{var}(X) = \int_{-\infty}^{\infty} x^2 f(x) \, dx - \mu^2$$

$$= \int_{-1}^{1} x^2 \frac{x+1}{2} \, dx - (\tfrac{1}{3})^2 = \frac{2}{9}$$

Proposition 5.2.1 A useful identity given constants a and b is

$$\text{var}(aX + b) = a^2 \text{var}(X)$$

PROOF
$$\begin{aligned}
\text{var}(aX + b) &= E[((aX + b) - (aE[X] + b))^2] \\
&= E[(aX - aE[X])^2] \\
&= E[a^2(X - E[X])^2] \\
&= a^2 E[(X - E[X])^2] \\
&= a^2 \text{var}(X)
\end{aligned}$$

Definition 5.2.4 If the random variable X has variance σ^2, then σ, the positive square root of the variance, is called the *standard deviation*.

Exercises 5.2

Exercise 5.2.1 For Exercise 2.3.1, compute $E(X)$ and $E(X^2)$. Use these results to find $E[(X+2)^2]$.

Exercise 5.2.2 For Exercise 2.3.3, find the mean A-level score and its variance.

Exercise 5.2.3 For Exercise 2.3.8, find $E(Z)$ and $E(Z^2)$.

Exercise 5.2.4 For Exercise 3.3.9, find $E[X]$, $E[X^2]$, var(X), $E[X^3]$.

Exercise 5.2.5 For Exercise 3.3.8, find $E[X]$, $E[X^2]$, var(X), $E[X^3]$.

Exercise 5.2.6 The random variable U has the probability density function

$$f_U(u) = \begin{cases} cue^{-au} & u > 0 \\ 0 & u < 0 \end{cases}$$

where c is a suitable constant.

(a) Find the constant c and sketch the graph of $f_U(u)$ against u.

(b) Find the distribution function $F_U(u)$ and sketch its graph.

(c) Find the expected value and variance of U.

(d) Find the expected value of $S = e^{-U}$.

(e) On your graph indicate the values u of U for which $S = e^{-U}$ is less than or equal to $\frac{1}{2}$. Hence or otherwise, find the probability that S is less than or equal to $\frac{1}{2}$.

Exercise 5.2.7 For Exercise 4.2.3, find $E[V]$ both directly from its marginal distribution and indirectly using the independence of X and Y.

Exercise 5.2.8 Find $E(X)$, $E(X^2)$ and var(X) for the density in Exercise 3.3.2.

Exercise 5.2.9 Evaluate $E(Y)$ for Exercise 3.3.3.

Exercise 5.2.10 Find $E(X)$ for Exercise 3.3.4.

5.3 MOMENTS OF SPECIAL DISTRIBUTIONS

Having introduced the general definitions of expectation we can now derive the mean and variance for some of the special discrete and continuous distributions introduced in the previous two chapters.

The binomial distribution

It is relatively straightforward to compute the expectation and variance of a random variable with binomial distribution. First notice that because the distribution we have specified exhausts all possible values it must be the case that the probabilities sum to one. This fact can be written as

$$\sum_{k=0}^{n} \binom{n}{k} p^k (1-p)^{n-k} = 1$$

Now consider the calculation of the expectation. This is defined as the sum of the products of the possible values with their respective probabilities; thus:

$$E(X) = \sum_{k=0}^{n} k \binom{n}{k} p^k (1-p)^{n-k}$$

$$= \sum_{k=1}^{n} \frac{n!}{(k-1)!(n-k)!} p^k (1-p)^{n-k}$$

(notice the change in the lower limit of the summation)

$$\sum_{k=1}^{n} np \frac{(n-1)!}{(k-1)!(n-k)!} p^{k-1} (1-p)^{n-k}$$

$$= np \sum_{j=0}^{m} \binom{m}{j} p^j (1-p)^{m-j}$$

where $m = n - 1$ and $j = k - 1$. The sum in the last line is just a sum of binomial probabilities and is therefore equal to 1. It follows that

$$E(X) = np$$

The variance may be computed using a similar argument as long as we notice initially that

$$\text{var } X = EX^2 - (EX)^2 = E(X^2 - X) + EX - (EX)^2$$
$$= E(X(X-1)) + EX - (EX)^2$$

Now

$$E(X(X-1)) = \sum_{k=2}^{n} k(k-1)\binom{n}{k} p^k (1-p)^{n-k}$$

$$= \sum_{k=2}^{n} \frac{n!}{(k-2)!(n-k)!} p^k (1-p)^{n-k}$$

$$= \sum_{k=2}^{n} n(n-1)p^2 \binom{n-2}{k-2} p^{k-2} (1-p)^{n-k}$$

$$= n(n-1)p^2$$

Therefore

$$\text{var } X = n(n-1)p^2 + np - n^2 p^2$$
$$= n^2 p^2 - np^2 + np - n^2 p^2$$
$$= np(1-p)$$

The Poisson distribution

The parameter λ in the Poisson distribution can be interpreted (by reference to the way in which we constructed it) as the probability of one arrival within the given interval of time or equivalently the average number of arrivals within the given interval. We can check this interpretation by deriving the mathematical expectation in the usual way:

$$E(X) = \sum_{k=0}^{\infty} k \frac{\lambda^k}{k!} e^{-\lambda}$$

$$= \lambda \sum_{k=1}^{\infty} \frac{\lambda^{k-1}}{(k-1)!} e^{-\lambda}$$

$$= \lambda \sum_{j=0}^{\infty} \frac{\lambda^j}{j!} e^{-\lambda} = \lambda$$

where $j = k - 1$ and the last equality is justified by the fact that the summation in the last line is a sum of Poisson probabilities and must therefore equal unity.

The variance can be computed by using the same device as we used in computing the variance of a binomially distributed random variable.

$$E(X(X-1)) = \sum_{k=0}^{\infty} k(k-1) \frac{\lambda^k}{k!} e^{-\lambda}$$

$$= \lambda^2 \sum_{k=2}^{\infty} \frac{\lambda^{k-2}}{(k-2)!} e^{-\lambda} = \lambda^2$$

$$\text{var } X = E(X(X-1)) + EX - (EX)^2$$

$$= \lambda^2 + \lambda - \lambda^2 = \lambda$$

The uniform distribution

The expectation of a random variable with rectangular distribution can be derived by integration in the usual way.

If X has the density function (uniform)

$$f(x) = \begin{cases} \dfrac{1}{b-a} & a < x < b \\ 0 & \text{elsewhere} \end{cases}$$

then

$$E[X] = \int_a^b \frac{x}{b-a} \, dx$$

$$= \frac{1}{b-a} \left[\frac{x^2}{2} \right]_a^b = \frac{1}{b-a} \left(\frac{b^2 - a^2}{2} \right)$$

$$= \frac{(b-a)(b+a)}{(b-a)^2}$$

$$= \frac{b+a}{2}$$

This is just the midpoint of the interval $[a, b]$ as common sense would suggest from the symmetrical shape of the distribution.

The variance can be derived directly by computing $E(X - EX)^2$ or by using the fact that var $X = E(X^2) - (EX)^2$. The first method works as follows:

$$
\begin{aligned}
\text{var } X &= E(X - EX)^2 \\
&= \int_a^b \left(x - \frac{a+b}{2} \right)^2 \frac{1}{b-a}\,dx \\
&= \frac{1}{b-a}\left[\frac{b^3 - a^3}{3} - \frac{(a+b)(b^2 - a^2)}{2} + \frac{(a+b)^2}{4}(b-a) \right]_a^b \\
&= \frac{1}{b-a}\left(\frac{b^3 - a^3}{3} - \frac{(a+b)(b^2 - a^2)}{2} + \frac{(a+b)^2}{4}(b-a) \right) \\
&= \frac{(a+b)^2}{3} - \frac{(a+b)^2}{2} + \frac{(a+b)^2}{4} - \frac{ab}{3} \\
&= \frac{(a+b)^2}{12} - \frac{ab}{3}
\end{aligned}
$$

The reader may want to check this result by following the second method.

The exponential distribution

A continuous random variable has an exponential distribution if its density function is

$$
f(x) = \begin{cases} \lambda\,e^{-\lambda x} & x > 0 \\ 0 & x \leqslant 0 \end{cases}
$$

Note that this random variable is always positive.

If X has an exponential distribution with parameter λ, then

$$
\begin{aligned}
E(X) &= \int_0^\infty x\lambda e^{-\lambda x}\,dx \\
&= \left[-\frac{\lambda x + 1}{\lambda} e^{-\lambda x} \right]_0^\infty \\
&= \frac{1}{\lambda}
\end{aligned}
$$

The variance can be shown to be var $X = 1/\lambda^2$. However, this is easier to demonstrate using moment generating functions, which we introduce in Section 5.7.

5.4 COVARIANCE AND CORRELATION

When we consider the joint distribution of two random variables, the means and the variances of the variables provide useful summary information on the marginal distributions of the random variables in question. However, these moment values do not provide any information on the nature of the relationship between the two random variables and whether they vary together or are independent. In this section we will introduce new concepts for measuring the association between two random variables. These concepts are familiar from the treatment of descriptive statistics in Book 1. In that volume the emphasis was on the computation and interpretation of measures of association between variables. In this section we wish to emphasize how the concepts of association are related to expectation.

Proposition 5.4.1 If X and Y are independent, then for any functions k and g,

$$E[g(X)k(Y))] = E[g(X)]E[k(Y)]$$

PROOF Since $f(x,y) = f_X(x) f_Y(y)$ then

$$E[g(X)k(Y)] = \int_{-\infty}^{\infty} \int_{-\infty}^{\infty} g(x)k(y)f_X(x)f_Y(y) \, dx \, dy$$

$$= \int_{-\infty}^{\infty} k(y)f_Y(y) \, dy \int_{-\infty}^{\infty} g(x)f_X(x) \, dx$$

$$= E[k(Y)] \, E[g(X)]$$

This result states that if two random variables are independent the expectation of the product of two functions of these random variables is equal to the expectation of the product of the same functions of the random variables.

One numerical measure of the association between two random variables is provided by the covariance between them.

Definition 5.4.1 The *covariance* between any two random variables X and Y, denoted by $\text{cov}(X, Y)$ is defined by

$$\text{cov}(X, Y) = E[(X - E[X])(Y - E[Y])]$$

This expression may be rearranged as

$$\text{cov}(X, Y) = E(XY - E[X]Y - XE[Y] + E[Y]E[X])$$
$$= E[XY] - E[X]E[Y] - E[X]E[Y] + E[X]E[Y]$$
$$= E[XY] - E[X]E[Y]$$

Note that if X and Y are independent then by Proposition 5.4.1, $E(XY) = E(X)E(Y)$. Hence,

$$\mathrm{cov}(X, Y) = 0$$

However, the converse is not necessarily true; variables with a covariance of zero may be dependent.

A useful result relating to the variance of the sum of two random variables is provided in the following proposition.

Proposition 5.4.2
$$\mathrm{var}(X + Y) = \mathrm{var}(X) + \mathrm{var}(Y) + 2\,\mathrm{cov}(X, Y).$$

PROOF
$$
\begin{aligned}
\mathrm{var}(X+Y) \\
&= E[(X+Y-E[X+Y])^2] \\
&= E[(X-E(X))+(Y-E(Y))^2] \\
&= E[(X-E(X))^2+(Y-E(Y))^2+2(X-E(X))(Y-E(Y))] \\
&= E[(X-E(X))^2]+E[(Y-E(Y))^2]+2E[(X-E(X))(Y-E(Y))] \\
&= \mathrm{var}(X) + \mathrm{var}(Y) + 2\,\mathrm{cov}(X, Y).
\end{aligned}
$$

The extension of the result in Proposition 5.4.2 to more than two random variables is provided by the following corollary.

Corollary 5.4.3

$$\mathrm{var}\left(\sum_{i=1}^{n} X_i\right) = \sum_{i=1}^{n} \mathrm{var}(X_i) + 2\sum_{i<j}\sum \mathrm{cov}(X_i, X_j).$$

Corollary 5.4.4 If $X_1, \ldots, X_n$ are independent then the $\mathrm{cov}(X_i, X_j) = 0$, hence

$$\mathrm{var}\left(\sum_{i=1}^{n} X_i\right) = \sum_{i=1}^{n} \mathrm{var}(X_i)$$

A simple measure of association for two random variables that is often used is the Pearson correlation coefficient. In Book 1 we showed that such a simple statistic may be very useful in assessing the nature of the association between two sets of numbers. At this juncture it is important to define this concept more formally.

Definition 5.4.2 The *correlation coefficient* of two random variables X and Y, denoted by $\varrho(X, Y)$ is defined as

$$\varrho(X, Y) = \frac{\mathrm{cov}(X, Y)}{\sqrt{\mathrm{var}(X)\,\mathrm{var}(Y)}}$$

where $\mathrm{var}(X), \mathrm{var}(Y) > 0$.

Proposition 5.4.5 It can be shown that

$$-1 \leqslant \varrho(X, Y) \leqslant 1$$

PROOF A proof of this result is beyond the scope of this text but can be found in more advanced books, e.g. Ross (1984, pp. 267–268).

Example 5.4.1 Let random variables X and Y have the joint probability density function

$$f(x, y) = \begin{cases} x + y & 0 < x < 1, 0 < y < 1 \\ 0 & \text{elsewhere} \end{cases}$$

Compute $\varrho(X, Y)$:

$$E[X] = \int_0^1 \int_0^1 x(x + y) \, dx \, dy = \tfrac{7}{12}$$

$$\text{var}(X) = E[X^2] - \mu_x^2$$

$$= \int_0^1 \int_0^1 x^2(x + y) \, dx \, dy - (\tfrac{7}{12})^2$$

$$= \tfrac{11}{144}$$

Similarly,

$$E(Y) = \tfrac{7}{12} \quad \text{and} \quad \text{var}(Y) = E(Y^2) - \mu_y^2 = \tfrac{11}{144}$$

$$\text{cov}(X, Y) = E(XY) - E(X)E(Y)$$

$$= \int_0^1 \int_0^1 xy(x + y) \, dx \, dy - (\tfrac{7}{12})^2 = \tfrac{-1}{144}$$

$$\varrho = \frac{\text{cov}(X, Y)}{\sigma_x \sigma_y} = \frac{\tfrac{-1}{144}}{\sqrt{(\tfrac{11}{144})(\tfrac{11}{144})}} = \tfrac{-1}{11}$$

5.5 CONDITIONAL EXPECTATION

In the previous chapter we introduced and described the general nature of bivariate distributions. In the course of that discussion we introduced the concept of a conditional density function and described how such a density function had all the usual properties associated with a conventional density function. Since we can define a conditional density function in the standard way it follows that we can define a conditional expectation in the analogous way that we have just done for a univariate density. Such a concept has the conventional interpretation except that the expectation we are now considering relates to the density of one random variable given a specific value of a second random variable. At this point it is appropriate to introduce some formal definitions.

Definition 5.5.1 If X and Y are discrete random variables the *conditional expectation* of X given $Y = y$ is

$$E[X|Y = y] = \sum_x x p_{X|Y}(x|y)$$

where $p_{X|Y}(x|y) = \dfrac{p(x,y)}{p_Y(y)}$ and $p_Y(y) > 0$

Likewise, if X and Y are continuous random variables,

$$E[X|Y = y] = \int_{-\infty}^{\infty} x f_{X|Y}(x,y)\,dx$$

where $f_{X|Y}(x|y) = \dfrac{f(x,y)}{f_Y(y)}$ and $f_Y(y) > 0$

Therefore the concept of a conditional expectation for a conditional density is directly analogous to that of an expectation for an ordinary density. That is to say, the conditional expectation is provided by computing the weighted average of the possible values of the conditional random variable, where the weights are provided by the conditional density.

Example 5.5.1 Let X and Y have the joint probability density function:

$$f(x,y) = \begin{cases} 2 & 0 < x < y < 1 \\ 0 & \text{elsewhere} \end{cases}$$

$$f_X(x) = \int_x^1 2\,dy = \begin{cases} 2(1-x) & 0 < x < 1 \\ 0 & \text{elsewhere} \end{cases}$$

and $$f_Y(y) = \int_0^y 2\,dx = \begin{cases} 2y & 0 < y < 1 \\ 0 & \text{elsewhere} \end{cases}$$

The conditional probability density function of X given $Y = y$ is

$$f(x|y) = \frac{2}{2y} = \begin{cases} \dfrac{1}{y} & 0 < x < y, \, 0 < y < 1 \\ 0 & \text{elsewhere} \end{cases}$$

Then the conditional mean of X given Y is

$$E(X|Y) = \int_{-\infty}^{\infty} x f(x|y)\,dx$$

$$= \int_0^y x\left(\frac{1}{y}\right)dx$$

$$= \frac{y}{2} \qquad 0 < y < 1$$

Proposition 5.5.1 $E[X] = E[E[X|Y]]$

PROOF The proof of this proposition is beyond the scope of this text but can be found in, for example, Ross (1984, p. 273).

The expectation of X can be thought of as the conditional expectation of X given Y weighted by that conditional distribution.

Since a conditional density is a conventional density in its own right it also has a variance associated with the conditional random variable. This conditional variance has a definition analogous to that for the variance of a conventional random variable, i.e. a conditional variance is the weighted sum of the squared deviations from the conditional mean.

Definition 5.5.2 The conditional variance of X given Y may be defined as

$$\operatorname{var}(X|Y) = E[[X - E(X|Y)]^2|Y]$$

The $\operatorname{var}(X|Y)$ is exactly analogous to the usual definition of variance, except that all expectations are conditional on the fact that Y is known.

Returning to Example 5.5.1, the conditional variance of X given y is

$$E[(X - E[X|Y])^2|y] = \int_0^y \left(x - \frac{y}{2}\right)^2 \left(\frac{1}{y}\right) dx$$

$$= \frac{y^2}{12} \qquad 0 < y < 1$$

Evaluate

$$E[X|Y = \tfrac{1}{2}] = \tfrac{1}{4}$$

Evaluate

$$P(0 < X < \tfrac{1}{2}|Y = \tfrac{3}{4}) = \int_0^{\frac{1}{2}} f(X|y = \tfrac{3}{4}) dx$$

$$= \int_0^{\frac{1}{2}} (\tfrac{4}{3}) dx = \tfrac{2}{3}$$

A final useful result which provides an additional expression for the variance of a random variable in terms of conditional expectation is stated in Proposition 5.5.2.

Proposition 5.5.2

$$\operatorname{var}(X) = E[\operatorname{var}(X|Y)] + \operatorname{var}(E[X|Y])$$

PROOF From Definition 5.2.3,

$$\text{var}(X|Y) = E[X^2|Y] - (E[X|Y])^2$$

so

$$E[\text{var}(X|Y)] = E[E[X^2|Y] - (E[X|Y])^2]$$
$$= E[X^2] - E[(E[X|Y])^2] \qquad *$$

Also, since

$$E[E[X|Y]] = E[X]$$

then

$$\text{var}(E[X|Y]) = E[(E[X|Y])^2] - [E[X]^2] \qquad **$$

Adding equations * and ** gives the result.

Exercises 5.5

Exercise 5.5.1 For Exercise 4.2.1, find:
(a) $E[Y|X = 1]$ and $\text{var}[Y|X = 1]$.
(b) $E[X]$, $E[Y]$, $E[X^2]$, $E[Y^2]$, $E[XY]$, $E[2X + 3Y]$, $\text{cov}(X, Y)$, ϱ, $\text{var}(X + Y)$, $\text{var}(2X - 3Y)$.
(c) How will you verify the result $\text{var}(Y) = E[\text{var}(Y|X)] + \text{var}(E[Y|X])$?

Exercise 5.5.2 For Exercise 4.2.7, find $E[X]$, $E[Y]$, $\text{var}(X)$, $\text{var}(Y)$, $\text{cov}(X, Y)$, ϱ, $E[X|Y = \frac{1}{2}]$, $\text{var}[X|Y = \frac{1}{2}]$. Are X and Y independent?

Exercise 5.5.3 For Exercise 4.2.8, find $E[X]$, $E[Y]$, $\text{var}(X)$, $\text{var}(Y)$, $\text{cov}(X, Y)$, ϱ, $E[X|Y = \frac{1}{2}]$, $\text{var}[X|Y = \frac{1}{2}]$. Are X and Y independent?

Exercise 5.5.4 Let the joint density of two continuous random variables X and Y be

$$f(x, y) = \begin{cases} 2 & 0 < x < y, 0 < y < 1 \\ 0 & \text{elsewhere} \end{cases}$$

(a) Find the marginal densities of X and Y.
(b) Find the conditional densities of X given Y and Y and given X. Show that the conditional means are respectively $(1 + X)/2$, $0 < x < 1$, and $y/2$, $0 < y < 1$.
(c) Evaluate the means and variances of X and Y.
(d) Show that the correlation coefficient between X and Y is $\varrho = \frac{1}{2}$.

*5.6 CHEBYSHEV'S THEOREM

In order to demonstrate how the standard deviation, σ, or variance, σ^2, is indicative of the dispersion of a distribution of a random variable we can prove Chebyshev's inequality. However, to derive this result we need first to prove Markov's inequality.

> **Proposition 5.6.1** Markov's inequality. If X is a random variable such that $P(X \geq 0) = 1$, then for any value $\alpha > 0$,
>
> $$P\{X \geq \alpha\} \leq \frac{E[X]}{\alpha}$$

PROOF

$$\begin{aligned}
E[X] &= \int_0^\infty xf(x)\,dx \\
&= \int_0^\alpha xf(x)\,dx + \int_\alpha^\infty xf(x)\,dx \\
&\geq \int_\alpha^\infty xf(x)\,dx \\
&\geq \int_\alpha^\infty \alpha f(x)\,dx \\
&= \alpha \int_\alpha^\infty f(x)\,dx \\
&= \alpha P\{X \geq \alpha\}
\end{aligned}$$

Theorem 5.6.1 Chebyshev's inequality. If X is a random variable with mean μ and variance σ^2, then for any $t > 0$,

$$P\{|X - \mu| \geq t\} \leq \frac{\sigma^2}{t^2}$$

PROOF Since $(X - \mu)^2$ is a non-negative r.v., we can apply Proposition 5.6.1 with $(\alpha = t^2)$ to give

$$P\{(X - \mu)^2 \geq t^2\} \leq \frac{E[(X - \mu)^2]}{t^2}$$

However, since $(X - \mu)^2 \geq t^2$ iff $|X - \mu| \geq t$, we can rewrite the above as

$$P\{|X - \mu| \geq t\} \leq \frac{E[(X - \mu)^2]}{t^2} = \frac{\sigma^2}{t^2}$$

The importance of these inequalities is that they enable us to compute bounds on the probabilities when only the mean or both the mean and variance of the probability distribution are known.

Example 5.6.1 It is possible to rewrite Chebyshev's inequality by substituting $\alpha = k^2\sigma^2$ and $X = (X - \mu)^2$ into Proposition 5.6.1:

$$P\{|X - \mu| \geq k\sigma\} \leq \frac{1}{k^2}$$

Hence

$$P\{|X - \mu| < k\sigma\} \geq 1 - \frac{1}{k^2}$$

Therefore

$$P[\mu - k\sigma < X < \mu + k\sigma] \geq 1 - \frac{1}{k^2}$$

So for $k = 2$ one gets

$$P[\mu - 2\sigma < X < \mu + 2\sigma] \geq \tfrac{3}{4}$$

i.e. for any random variable X with finite variance at least $\tfrac{3}{4}$ of the mass of X falls within two standard deviations of its mean. (This is why we were able to say in Chapter 1 that more than 75 per cent of people in the Lichtenstein and Newman survey lie in the $\pm 2\sigma$ range.)

Ordinarily to calculate the probability of an event described in terms of the random variable X, the probability density function (or cumulative distribution function) of X is needed. Chebyshev's inequality provides a lower bound probability statement for any random variable, X, which is sometimes very useful. However, the actual probability associated with an interval of X may be much greater. For example, for a normally distributed random variable over 95 per cent of the mass lies within two standard deviations of the mean.

*5.7 MOMENTS AND MOMENT GENERATING FUNCTIONS

So far in this chapter we have talked about the mean or expectation of a random variable as being its first moment. In fact, the concept of moments is much more general than this and requires clarification.

Definition 5.7.1 If X is a random variable then the numbers

$$\mu_k = E(X^k) \qquad k = 1, 2, \ldots$$

are called the *moments* of X.

Hence μ_1 is the first moment and μ_2 is the second moment and so on. You should of course notice that

$$\text{var}(X) = \mu_2 - \mu_1^2$$

Using our results on the expectation of a function of a random variable it is therefore possible to write an expression for computing the moments as

$$\mu_k = \int_{-\infty}^{\infty} x^k f(x)\, \mathrm{d}x$$

In general the moments of a distribution are very useful since they form the *basis* of measures of central tendency (the first moment), variability (the second moment), skewness (the third moment) and kurtosis (the fourth moment). Therefore it is important to be able to obtain the moments of any specific distribution fairly easily.

Although the moments of most distributions can be determined directly by evaluating the necessary integrals or summations there is an alternative procedure which is sometimes a more convenient method of analysis. This is based on the moment generating function.

Definition 5.7.2 A *moment generating function* $M(t)$ of the random variable X is defined for all real values of t by

$$M(t) = E[e^{tX}] = \begin{cases} \sum_x e^{tX} p(x) \\ \int_{-\infty}^{\infty} e^{tX} f(x)\, \mathrm{d}x \end{cases}$$

Depending on whether X is a discrete or continuous random variable $M(t)$ is called a moment generating function (m.g.f.) because all the moments of X can be obtained by successively differentiating $M(t)$ and evaluating the result at $t = 0$. To see this:

$$M'(t) = \frac{\mathrm{d}M(t)}{\mathrm{d}t} = \frac{\mathrm{d}}{\mathrm{d}t} E[e^{tX}]$$

$$= E\left[\frac{\mathrm{d}(e^{tX})}{\mathrm{d}t}\right]$$

$$= E[Xe^{tX}]$$

For our purpose we can assume that we can differentiate under the integral sign. Evaluating this expression at $t = 0$ gives

$$M'(0) = E[Xe^{tX}]_{t=0} = E[X]$$

Similarly,

$$M''(t) = \frac{d}{dt} M'(t)$$

$$= \frac{d}{dt} E[Xe^{tX}]$$

$$= E\left[\frac{d}{dt}(Xe^{tX})\right]$$

$$= E[X^2 e^{tX}]$$

and thus

$$M''(0) = E[X^2]$$

In general, the nth derivative of $M(t)$ is given by

$$M^n(t) = E[X^n e^{tX}] \qquad n \geq 1$$

implying $M^n(0) = E[X^n]$. Hence the name moment generating function. Note that

$$\text{var}(X) = M''(0) - [M'(0)]^2.$$

Example 5.7.1 If X is a random variable with a probability density function

$$f(x) = \begin{cases} e^{-x} & x > 0 \\ 0 & \text{elsewhere} \end{cases}$$

then

$$M(t) = E[e^{tX}] = \int_0^\infty e^{tx} e^{-x} \, dx$$

$$= \int_0^\infty e^{(t-1)x} \, dx$$

$$M(t) = \left[\frac{e^{(t-1)x}}{t-1}\right]_0^\infty$$

$$= -\left[\frac{1}{t-1}\right] = \frac{1}{1-t}$$

$$M'(t) = \frac{1}{(1-t)^2}$$

$$M''(t) = \frac{2}{(1-t)^3}$$

$$E[X] = M'(0) = 1$$

$$E[X^2] = M''(0) = 2$$

$$\text{var}(X) = M''(0) - [M'(0)]^2$$

$$= 1$$

Example 5.7.2 Looking back to our special distributions and recalling the exponential random variable with a probability density function

$$f(x) = \begin{cases} \lambda e^{-\lambda x} & x > 0 \\ 0 & \text{elsewhere} \end{cases}$$

then

$$M(t) = E[e^{tx}] = \int_0^\infty e^{tx} \lambda e^{-\lambda x}\, dx$$

$$= \int_0^\infty \lambda e^{(t-\lambda)x}\, dx$$

$$M(t) = \frac{\lambda}{\lambda - t}$$

$$M'(t) = \frac{\lambda}{(\lambda - t)^2}$$

$$M''(t) = \frac{2\lambda}{(\lambda - t)^3}$$

$$E[X] = M'(0) = 1/\lambda$$

$$E[X^2] = M''(0) = 2/\lambda^2$$

Therefore

$$\text{var}(X) = M''(0) - [M'(0)]^2$$

$$= \frac{2}{\lambda^2} - \left(\frac{1}{\lambda}\right)^2$$

$$= \frac{1}{\lambda^2}$$

Finally, we can now give the proof of Theorem 3.6.4, which stated that the sum of independent normally distributed random variables is a normally distributed random variable with mean equal to the sum of the means and variance equal to the sum of the variances of the original random variables. The proof of this uses the moment generating function approach. The m.g.f. of a $N(\mu, \sigma^2)$ distributed random variable is

$$\Psi(t) = \exp\left\{\mu t + \frac{\sigma^2 t^2}{2}\right\}$$

The m.g.f. of the sum of independent random variables is the product of their m.g.f.'s. Therefore if X_1 is $N(\mu_1, \sigma_1^2)$ and X_2 is $N(\mu_2, \sigma_2^2)$ then

$$\Psi(t) = \exp(\mu_1 t + \tfrac{1}{2}\sigma_1^2 t^2)\exp(\mu_2 t + \tfrac{1}{2}\sigma_2^2 t^2)$$

$$= \exp[(\mu_1 + \mu_2)t + \tfrac{1}{2}(\sigma_1^2 + \sigma_2^2)t^2]$$

which is the m.g.f. of a normally distributed random variable with mean $(\mu_1 + \mu_2)$ and variance $(\sigma_1^2 + \sigma_2^2)$.

Exercises 5.7

Exercise 5.7.1 Find the moment generating function for the problem in Exercise 3.3.1. Evaluate $E(X)$ and var(X).

Exercise 5.7.2 Find the moment generating function for the problem in Exercise 3.3.2. Evaluate $E(X)$ and $E(X^2)$.

Exercise 5.7.3 (*a*) Write down the moment generating function for the bivariate normal distribution. Derive the expression for the means of the two random variables and their correlation coefficient from this moment generating function.

   (*b*) Using the m.g.f. show that if the correlation coefficient is zero the two random variables are independent.

Exercise 5.7.4 (continuation of Exercise 3.7.4) (*a*) Use the moment generating function method to show that the sum of n independent exponentially distributed random variables, each with parameter λ, has a $\Gamma(n, \lambda)$ distribution.

   (*b*) Deduce that the sum of two independent random variables distributed as $\Gamma(n_1, \lambda)$ and $\Gamma(n_2, \lambda)$ has a $\Gamma(n_1 + n_2, \lambda)$ distribution.

GUIDE TO FURTHER READING AND COMPUTER SOFTWARE

GUIDE TO FURTHER READING

Details of the books mentioned here are given in the next section, 'References'. For those interested in a gentle introduction to the subject of statistics, in the historical origins of the subject, or in biographical details of the eminent statisticians, the book by Kennedy (1983) is very readable.

The books by Yeomans (1968) and Fuller and Lury (1977) are good introductions to descriptive statistics.

There are many introductory books that cover only probability theory. The books by Arthurs (1965), Gnedenko and Khinchin (1961), Rozanov (1969) and Chung (1974) all have different things to recommend them. The books by Lipschutz (1974) and Rowntree (1984) are introductory volumes with a large number of questions and worked examples.

Those interested in more advanced texts on estimation, inference and hypothesis testing would be well advised to look at De Groot (1975).

For students of economics wishing to use statistics in their subject a good starting place is Thomas (1983).

Examples of A-level standard textbooks are Clarke and Cooke (1978), Francis (1983), Crawshaw and Chambers (1984) and Miller (1983).

Examples of standard first year undergraduate texts are Mood, Graybill and Boes (1974), Meyer (1970), Hogg and Craig (1978) and Larson (1982).

There are many texts of a similar level to the present one. Among these are the books by Strait (1983) and Freund and Walpole (1980). At the slightly more advanced level the books by Ross (1984) has been referred to many times and is a good treatment of probability at the intermediate level. The reader in search of even higher level texts on probability should consult Feller (1968) and Parzen (1960).

If you seek good references which concisely describe the probability distributions and their statistics the books by Govil (1984) and Hastings and Peacock (1974) can both be recommended.

OTHER COMPUTER SOFTWARE

There is a variety of other statistics computer software designed for use with microcomputers. Most of this software is in such a form that it will compute your statistics for you, given your data. Three examples of packages of this kind are:

Unistat II, published by UNISOFT Limited
BM.STAT, published by International Software
Instat, produced by the University of Reading

A second category of software is of the kind that enables the user to perform simulations and demonstrations. A good example of such software is

A-level STATISTICS, published by the BBC and written by V. Barnett and P. Holmes at the Centre for Statistical Education

Two prominent packages in use on both the IBM PC and most mainframe computers are SPSS-X and MINITAB. Both of these packages provide excellent facilities for the calculation of descriptive statistics and the estimation of statistical models.

The text and software by Robinson and Bowman (1986) is also worth looking at.

A third kind of software is a more general catalogue of statistical and numerical algorithms which may be used in the writing of your own programs. One example of such software is well described in the book by Cooke, Craven and Clarke (1982). These programs are available separately on disk but are written in simple BASIC.

Other books that contain programs and algorithms are those by Whittle (1985) (covers all A-level mathematics, not just statistics) and Groeneveld (1979), Lee and Lee (1982) and Tennant-Smith (1985).

Those specifically interested in computer simulation in statistics should look at the book by Morgan (1984) which also contains many programs written in BASIC.

REFERENCES

Arthurs, A. M. (1965) *Probability Theory*, Routledge & Kegan Paul, London.

Binmore, K. G. (1982) *Mathematical Analysis: A Straightforward Approach*, Cambridge University Press.

Central Statistical Office. *Annual Abstract of Statistics*, HMSO, London.

Central Statistical Office. *Social Trends*, HMSO, London.

Chapman, M. and B. Mahon (1986) *Plain Figures*, HMSO, London.

Chung, K. L. (1974) *Elementary Probability Theory with Stochastic Processes*, Springer Verlag, Berlin.

Clarke, G. M. and D. Cooke (1978) *A Basic Course in Statistics*, Edward Arnold, London.

Cooke, D., A. H. Craven and G. M. Clarke (1982) *Basic Statistical Computing*, Edward Arnold, London.

Crawshaw, J. and J. Chambers (1984) *A Course in A Level Statistics*, Stanley Thornes, Cheltenham.

De Groot, M. (1975) *Probability and Statistics*, Addison-Wesley, Wokingham.

Department of Employment. *Employment Gazette*, HMSO, London.

Feller, W. (1968) *An Introduction to Probability Theory and Its Applications*, vol I, 3rd edn, John Wiley & Sons, Chichester.

Francis, A. (1983) *Advanced Level Statistics: An Integrated Course*, Stanley Thornes, Cheltenham.

Freund, J. and R. Walpole (1980) *Mathematical Statistics*, Prentice-Hall, Hemel Hempstead.

Fuller, M. F. and D. A. Lury (1977) *Statistics Workbook for Social Science Students*, Philip Allan, Oxford.

Gnedenko, B. V. and A. Y. Khinchin (1961) *An Elementary Introduction to the Theory of Probability*, Freeman, Oxford.

Govil, A. K. (1984) *Definitions and Formulae in Statistics*, 2nd edn, Macmillan, London.

Groeneveld, R. A. (1979) *An Introduction to Probability and Statistics Using BASIC*, Marcel Dekker, New York.

Hastings, N. A. J. and J. B. Peacock (1974) *Statistical Distributions*, John Wiley & Sons, Chichester.

Hogg, R. and A. Craig (1978) *Introduction to Mathematical Statistics*, 4th edn, Collier-Macmillan, London.

Jeffreys, H. (1939) *Theory of Probability*, Oxford University Press.

148

Kendall, Sir M. and A. Stuart (1977) *The Advanced Theory of Statistics*, 4th edn, Charles Griffen & Co., London.

Kennedy, G. (1983) *Invitation to Statistics*, Martin Robertson & Co., Oxford.

Keynes, J. M. (1921) *Treatise on Probability*, Collected Writings, vol. 7, Macmillan, London.

Larson, M. J. (1982) *Introduction to Probability Theory and Statistical Inference*. 3rd edn, John Wiley & Sons, Chichester.

Lee, J. D. and T. D. Lee (1982) *Statistics and Computer Methods in BASIC*, Van Nostrand Reinhold, Wokingham.

Lichtenstein, S. and J. R. Newman (1967) 'Empirical scaling of common verbal phrases associated with numerical probabilities', *Psychonomic Science*, vol. 9, pp. 563–564.

Lipschutz, S. (1974) *Probability: Theory and Problems*, Schaum Outline Series, McGraw-Hill, London.

McGregor, J. and A. Watt (1983a) *The BBC Micro Book: Basic, Sound and Graphics*, Addison-Wesley, Wokingham.

McGregor, J. and Watt, A. (1983b) *Advanced Programming Techniques for the BBC Micro*, Addison-Wesley, Wokingham.

Meyer, P. L. (1970) *Introductory Probability and Statistical Applications*, 2nd edn, Addison-Wesley, Wokingham.

Miller, J. (1983) *Statistics for Advanced Level*, Cambridge University Press.

Mokyr, J. (1983) *Why Ireland Starved*, Allen & Unwin, London.

Mood, A., F. Graybill and D. Boes (1974) *Introduction to the Theory of Statistics*, 3rd edn, McGraw-Hill, London.

Morgan, B. J. T. (1984) *Elements of Simulation*, Chapman & Hall, London.

Office of Population Censuses and Surveys. *Census 1981: Housing and Households in England and Wales*, HMSO, London.

Parzen, E. (1960) *Modern Probability Theory and Its Applications*, John Wiley & Sons, Chichester.

Robinson, D. R. and A. W. Bowman (1986) *Introduction to Probability: A Computer Illustrated Text*, Adam Hilger, Bristol.

Ross, S. (1984) *A First Course in Probability Theory*, 2nd edn, Collier-Macmillan, London.

Rowntree, D. (1984) *Probability*, Edward Arnold, London.

Rozanov, Y. A. (1969) *Probability Theory*, Dover, New York.

Strait, P. L. (1983) *A First Course in Probability and Statistics with Applications*, Harcourt Brace Jovanovich, New York.

Tennant-Smith, J. (1985) *BASIC Statistics*, Butterworth, Sevenoaks.

Thomas, J. J. (1983) *An Introduction to Statistical Analysis for Economists*, 2nd edn, Weidenfeld & Nicholson, London.

Whittle, A. (1985) *Mathematical Programs in BBC BASIC*, Prentice-Hall, Hemel Hempstead.

Williamson, P. (1981) *The Early Careers of Graduates*, Research paper no. 26, Department of Employment.

Yeomans, K. A. (1968) *Introducing Statistics: Statistics for the Social Scientist*, vols 1 and 2, Penguin, Harmondsworth.

DESCRIPTION OF THE PROGRAMS AVAILABLE WITH THIS BOOK†

This software contains 'descriptive' and 'interactive' programs, distinguished by their content and level of student involvement. The descriptive programs outline the basic principles of a particular topic with the intention of giving an introduction to the subject matter covered. The interactive programs involve the students more than the descriptive programs and test their knowledge or enrich their understanding of the material. The programs use the excellent graphics and simulation capabilities of the computer to present material in an attractive way. As far as possible or sensible, the data are either generated at random or a choice of data is offered so that the detail of each run can change from one run to the next, thus providing greater variety and interest. The programs are self-contained and self-explanatory and, in principle, can be studied without further reading, but their use in conjunction with the book is recommended.

PROBABILITY I

1. Set theory   This descriptive program introduces all the basic set theory definitions with the aid of Venn diagrams. All the concepts of set theory necessary to follow the content of the text are defined in this program. (Section 1.3)

2. Set theory example   The program uses the definitions of set theory to explore an example in some detail. The analysis is presented graphically. (Example 1.3.3)

† See Appendix C for a complete catalogue of programs available with Books 1, 2 and 3.

3. Venn diagrams This is an interactive program which allows the student to draw set theoretic expressions in Venn diagrams. Detailed instructions for the use of this program are presented on pages 155–156 of this Appendix and on the screen in the program.

4. Words and probability This interactive program allows you to explore the relation between words describing uncertainty and probability and the numerical values which people may attach to such phrases. You are asked to evaluate a word or phrase and attach the probability number which most clearly reflects the degree of probability implied by that word or phrase. Your opinion is then compared with research of two psychologists Lichtenstein and Newman who used the same technique with 184 people and summarized the results. This program should provoke you to think about the relation between words and numbers and different people's assessment of them. The program is also useful in providing another example of the use of summary statistics. (Section 1.1)

5. Probability as a frequency This interactive program allows you to simulate the tossing of a fair coin. If you provide the computer with a number of trials the computer will perform the simulation and graph the relative proportion of heads which occur. This program therefore provides an insight into the nature of repeated trials and simulation. (Section 1.2)

6. Subjective probability This program provides an insight into the concept of subjective probability. The interactive program asks you to imagine that you are firing a gun which will always hit a square target of unit size. Within the target there is an irregular-shaped random-lighted area. Assume that you have no control over the precise direction of the gun (except that it will always hit somewhere in the square). You are then asked what is the probability of hitting a particular shape in the lighted area. (Section 1.1)

PROBABILITY II

7. Combinational analysis This descriptive program introduces the concepts of permutations and combinations and explains them. (Section 1.4)

8. Axioms of probability This program provides an introduction to the axioms of probability. The program is descriptive but allows you to go through the proofs of the main results of basic probability theory at your own speed. (Section 4.5)

9. Conditional probability This program introduces conditional probability. The program uses Venn diagrams and other graphical devices to explain the concepts, with the use of Example 1.6.2. The program is descriptive. (Section 1.6)

10. Bayes' theorem This program provides an exposition of Bayes' theorem which allows you to understand the proof of the result at your own speed. (Section 1.6)

11. Permutations and combinations This interactive program allows you to compute your own problem of permutations or combinations. You may choose, via a menu, which kind of problem you wish to compute and you are then prompted for details. The computer will then return the answer to your problem.

12. Independence In this interactive program you can explore the concept of independence. The program allows you to specify upper bounds on four variables A, B, C, and D. You are then asked to enter two arithmetic expressions (X and Y) in terms of A, B, C and D. The program then assesses the truth of the X or Y expression for all values that the variables may take. The results are then tabulated in terms of the probabilities of $P(X)$, $P(Y)$, $P(P \cap Y)$, $P(X \cup Y)$, $P(X|Y)$, $P(X) \cdot P(Y)$ and the independence of the events X and Y is assessed.

RANDOM VARIABLES AND DISTRIBUTION THEORY

13. Discrete random variables This descriptive program follows the exposition in Section 2.3 which relates to a coin tossing example. The concepts of a random variable, probability function and a cumulative distribution function are introduced and explained in the context of this example. (Section 2.3)

14. Discrete random variables: dice example This program explores the discrete random variable example presented in the text. This example relates to the tossing of two coins and graphically derives and explains the probability and cumulative distribution functions of this example. (Sections 2.2 and 2.3)

15. Continuous random variables This program provides a graphical treatment of continuous random variables by showing the relation between the probability density function and the cumulative distribution function. (Sections 3.2 and 3.3)

16. Continuous random variables: archery example This program is designed to help you understand the process by which we can model random variables in a continuous manner. By simulating the archer's problem of firing at a target and plotting a score as a histogram we can build up a picture of the probability distribution of the score. As the simulation is performed a large number of times this probability function should approach a continuous random variable.

17. Dice and histograms This interactive program allows you to simulate the throwing of several dice and graphically compares the actual distribution of the sum of the dice with the theoretical probability distribution over that score.

18. Archery example This interactive program allows the user to explore further the archery problem posed in Program 16 by allowing you to simulate the problem for yourself, assuming you are either an experienced archer or a novice archer and allowing you to determine the number of shots at the target. The frequency distribution of the score can then be plotted for 10 or 20 intervals.

SPECIAL DISTRIBUTIONS I

19. Binomial distribution: theory This descriptive program uses an example to illustrate the construction and interpretation of binomial probabilities. The concept of Bernoulli trials is introduced and several examples given. The binomial probabilities are explained as giving the probabilities of different numbers of successes in a sequence of Bernoulli trials. Finally, tabular and graphical modes of presentation are described.

20. Binomial distribution: interactive This program displays binomial distribution for user-selected parameter values, and presents a summary based on the skewness of the distribution.

21. Poisson distribution: theory A descriptive program showing how the Poisson distribution can be derived as a special case of the binomial where p is small and n is large. Interpretation of the parameter is discussed briefly, and the distribution is presented in graphic and tabular form for various values of the parameter.

22. Poisson distribution: interactive This program enables investigation of the changing shape of the distribution as the parameter value changes; also gives a summary showing skewness as a function of the parameter.

SPECIAL DISTRIBUTIONS II

23. Rectangular distribution: theory   This descriptive program uses the example of a well balanced pointer to illustrate the rectangular density function and its use; the function is displayed graphically and algebraically. Probabilities are recovered from it geometrically and by integration.

24. Rectangular distribution: interactive   This program provides practice in computing probabilities from a continuous density function.

25. Exponential distribution: theory   This short description uses graphics and algebra of the exponential distribution.

26. Exponential distribution: interactive   This program enables the user to examine the effect on the exponential density function of changing the value of its parameter.

27. Normal distribution

27.1 Theory   The program gives a description of the density function and geometric interpretation of its parameters; discussion of the algebraic form noting the difficulty of explicit integration; transformation to standard normal.

27.2 Interactive   An introduction to the probability calculator.

27.3 Normal approximations: theory   This is an expository treatment of normal approximation to the binomial, showing how the error falls as n increases, and distinguishing two sources of error.

27.4 Normal approximations: interactive   Normal approximations to Binomial and Poisson distributions can be investigated by means of user selection of parameters.

27.5 Central limit theorem   This program uses an example with Bernoulli random variables to demonstrate this theorem.

27.6 Probability calculator

28. Approximations

28.1 Poisson approximation to Binomial: theory   Descriptive program showing how Poisson probabilities can be used to approximate Binomial probabilities when n is large and p is small.

28.2 Poisson approximation to Binomial: interactive For user-selected parameter values, the error in the Poisson approximation is shown.

BIVARIATE DISTRIBUTIONS AND EXPECTATION

29. Bivariate discrete distributions: more on dice This program introduces jointly distributed random variables by first considering a simple discrete example using two dice. (Section 4.2)

30. Continuous bivariate distributions: more on archery This descriptive program explains the concepts associated with continuous bivariate distributions by using Example 4.2.2.

31. Functions of random variables This descriptive program explains the derivation of a function of a single random variable using an example in a '3 quadrant' diagram. (Section 4.4)

32. Expectation This descriptive program explains the concept of the expectation of a random variable. (Section 5.2)

33. The bivariate normal distribution This is an interactive program which allows you to draw a 'mesh plot' of a bivariate normal distribution of your own choosing. The program asks you for values of σ_x, σ_y, ϱ, the standard deviation of X and Y and the correlation coefficient between them and then draws the 3D plot of what this surface looks like. (Section 4.3)

ADDITIONAL NOTES FOR PROGRAM 3: VENN DIAGRAMS

An annotated version of the information below appears on the screen.

Introduction

This interactive program uses Venn diagrams to permit you to evaluate set theory expressions. Three sets A, B and C are drawn (enclosing eight segments on the screen) which allow you to represent any standard set theory expression by highlighting the relevant area in *red*.

Keys and symbols

The full set of symbols used and their corresponding keystrokes is:

Key	*Screen symbol*	*Meaning*
A	A	the set A
B	B	the set B
C	C	the set C
'	'	the complement of what precedes
&	∩	and, i.e. the intersection of
U	∪	or, i.e. the union of
0 (zero)	∅	the NULL set
S	S	the Universal set or Space
( )	( )	the use of brackets is permitted

Instructions

Initially the program displays a Venn diagram of three overlapping sets A, B and C and invites you to enter an expression. After each expression you are invited to enter another to be evaluated.

In entering expressions a few simple rules must be observed:

1. Capital letters will always be used.
2. If parentheses are used then they must be matched and make sense, e.g. AUB is invalid, (AUB) is acceptable.
3. Use only the prescribed character set, i.e. A, B, C, ', &(∩), U(∪), 0, S, (,).
4. Spaces are ignored and therefore may be included or excluded without affecting the result.
5. Double complements adjacent to one another without a bracket, i.e. ", should be avoided. Hence A'' is unacceptable $(A')'$ is permitted. Expressions like $(A' \cup B)'$ are also obviously acceptable.
6. On the BBC computer the intersection operator, ∩, has precedence over the union operator, ∪, in a composite expression. On the IBM computer the intersection and union operators have equal precedence. Use a bracket to make your intentions clear.

Therefore the expression

$$A \cap B \cup C \quad \text{and} \quad C \cup (B \cap A)$$

both take intersection of A and B first then join this in union with the set C.

If you wished to take the union of C and B first and then find its intersection with A you should write

$$(C \cup B) \cap A.$$

B
PROPERTIES OF DISTRIBUTIONS AND STATISTICAL TABLES

Tables B.1 and B.2 set out the probability density function, mean, variance and moment generating function for each distribution used in the text. Some notes on the interrelations between the distributions are also provided. Readers who require more detail on the properties of these distributions (and more complex distributions) should consult Hastings and Peacock (1974) and Govil (1984).

Tables B.3 and B.4 (reproduced with permission from John Wiley & Sons Inc., New York) give areas of a standard normal distribution and Student's-t distribution, respectively.

B.1 SOME DISCRETE DISTRIBUTIONS

Name and parameters	Probability function	Mean	Variance	Moment generating function	Notes
Uniform $U[a,b]$	$f(x) = 1/b$ $a \leq x \leq a+b-1, x$ integer	$\dfrac{a+b-1}{2}$	$\dfrac{b^2-1}{12}$		
Binomial $b(n,p)$	$f(x) = \binom{n}{p} p^x (1-p)^{n-x}$ $0 \leq x \leq n, x$ integer $0 \leq p \leq 1$	np	$np(1-p)$	$[p\exp(t) + (1-p)]^n$	b can be approximated by $p(\lambda)$ with $\lambda = np$ if p is small, that is $p < 0.1$. b can also be approximated by $N(\mu, \sigma^2)$ with $\mu = np, \sigma^2 = npq$ if $np > 5$ and $0.1 \leq p \leq 0.9$ or if $np > 25$.
Poisson $p(\lambda)$	$f(x) = e^{-\lambda} \dfrac{\lambda^x}{x!}$ $x \leq 0, x$ integer $\lambda > 0$	λ	λ	$\exp\{\lambda[\exp(t) - 1]\}$	p is the limiting form of b as $n \to \infty, p \to 0$ and $np \to \lambda$.

B.2 SOME CONTINUOUS DISTRIBUTIONS

Name and parameters	Probability density function	Mean	Variance	Moment generating function	Notes
Uniform $U[\alpha,\beta]$	$f(x) = 1/(\beta - \alpha)$ $\alpha \leq x \leq \beta$	$\dfrac{\alpha + \beta}{2}$	$\dfrac{(\beta - \alpha)^2}{12}$	$\dfrac{e^{\alpha t} e^{(\beta t)^{-1}}}{\beta t}$	
Normal $N[\mu,\sigma^2]$	$f(x) = \dfrac{1}{\sigma\sqrt{2\pi}} e^{\left[-\frac{(x-\mu)^2}{2\sigma^2}\right]}$ $-\infty \leq x \leq \infty, \sigma > 0$	μ	σ^2	$e^{\mu t + \sigma^2 t^2/2}$	If $z = (x - \mu)/\sigma$ the z is $N(0,1)$ and is referred to as the standard normal.
Exponential with parameter λ	$f(x) = \lambda e^{-\lambda x}$ $x \geq 0, \lambda > 0$	$\dfrac{1}{\lambda}$	$\dfrac{1}{\lambda^2}$	$\dfrac{1}{1 - bt}$ $b = \dfrac{1}{\lambda}, t > \dfrac{1}{b}$	Exponential $E(\lambda)$ is $\Gamma(1,\lambda)$ $[E(X)$ is $-\lambda \log U(0,1)]$. Also the sum of n exponential variables $E_i(\lambda); i = 1,\ldots,t$ is $\Gamma(t,\lambda)$ distributed.

Gamma $\Gamma(\alpha,\lambda)$	$f(x) = \dfrac{x^{\lambda-1}e^{(-x/\alpha)}}{\alpha^\lambda\,\Gamma(\lambda)}$ $x \geq 0,\, a > 0,\, \lambda > 0$ where the gamma function is $\Gamma(\lambda) = \displaystyle\int_0^\infty e^{-y}y^{\lambda-1}\,\mathrm{d}y$	$a\lambda$	$a^2\lambda$	$(1-at)^{-\lambda}$ $t > \dfrac{1}{\lambda}$	If λ is such that 2λ is an integer then x is $\tfrac{1}{2}\chi^2_\lambda$, i.e. chi-squared distributed.
Beta $\beta(a,b)$	$f(x) = \dfrac{1}{B(a,b)}x^{a-1}(1-x)^{b-1}$ $0 \leq x \leq 1,\, a > 0,\, b > 0$ where the beta function is $B(a,b) = \displaystyle\int_0^1 x^{a-1}(1-x)^{b-1}\,\mathrm{d}x$	$\dfrac{a}{a+b}$	$\dfrac{ab}{(a+b)^2(a+b+1)}$	Does not exist in closed form	$\beta(1,1)$ is U distributed.
Student's-t $t(n)$	$f(x) = \dfrac{\Gamma[(n+1)/2]}{\sqrt{(n\pi)}\,\Gamma(n/2)}\left(1+\dfrac{x^2}{n}\right)^{-(n+1)/2}$	0	$\dfrac{n}{n-2}$, $n > 2$	Does not exist	$f(x)$ converges to $N(x)$ for every x in $(-\infty, \infty)$ as $n \to \infty$; $t(1)$ is the Cauchy distribution.

B.3 AREAS OF A STANDARD NORMAL DISTRIBUTION

An entry in the table is the proportion under the entire curve which is
between $z = 0$ and a positive value of z. Areas for negative values of z are
obtained by symmetry.

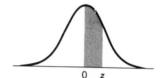

z	.00	.01	.02	.03	.04	.05	.06	.07	.08	.09
0.0	.0000	.0040	.0080	.0120	.0160	.0199	.0239	.0279	.0319	.0359
0.1	.0398	.0438	.0478	.0517	.0557	.0596	.0636	.0675	.0714	.0753
0.2	.0793	.0832	.0871	.0910	.0948	.0987	.1026	.1064	.1103	.1141
0.3	.1179	.1217	.1255	.1293	.1331	.1368	.1406	.1443	.1480	.1517
0.4	.1554	.1591	.1628	.1664	.1700	.1736	.1772	.1808	.1844	.1879
0.5	.1915	.1950	.1985	.2019	.2054	.2088	.2123	.2157	.2190	.2224
0.6	.2257	.2291	.2324	.2357	.2389	.2422	.2454	.2486	.2517	.2549
0.7	.2580	.2611	.2642	.2673	.2703	.2734	.2764	.2794	.2823	.2852
0.8	.2881	.2910	.2939	.2967	.2995	.3023	.3051	.3078	.3106	.3133
0.9	.3159	.3186	.3212	.3238	.3264	.3289	.3315	.3340	.3365	.3389
1.0	.3413	.3438	.3461	.3485	.3508	.3531	.3554	.3577	.3599	.3621
1.1	.3643	.3665	.3686	.3708	.3729	.3749	.3770	.3790	.3810	.3830
1.2	.3849	.3869	.3888	.3907	.3925	.3944	.3962	.3980	.3997	.4015
1.3	.4032	.4049	.4066	.4082	.4099	.4115	.4131	.4147	.4162	.4177
1.4	.4192	.4207	.4222	.4236	.4251	.4265	.4279	.4292	.4306	.4319
1.5	.4332	.4345	.4357	.4370	.4382	.4394	.4406	.4418	.4429	.4441
1.6	.4452	.4463	.4474	.4484	.4495	.4505	.4515	.4525	.4535	.4545
1.7	.4554	.4564	.4573	.4582	.4591	.4599	.4608	.4616	.4625	.4633
1.8	.4641	.4649	.4656	.4664	.4671	.4678	.4686	.4693	.4699	.4706
1.9	.4713	.4719	.4726	.4732	.4738	.4744	.4750	.4756	.4761	.4767
2.0	.4772	.4778	.4783	.4788	.4793	.4798	.4803	.4808	.4812	.4817
2.1	.4821	.4826	.4830	.4834	.4838	.4842	.4846	.4850	.4854	.4857
2.2	.4861	.4864	.4868	.4871	.4875	.4878	.4881	.4884	.4887	.4890
2.3	.4893	.4896	.4898	.4901	.4904	.4906	.4909	.4911	.4913	.4916
2.4	.4918	.4920	.4922	.4925	.4927	.4929	.4931	.4932	.4934	.4936
2.5	.4938	.4940	.4941	.4943	.4945	.4946	.4948	.4949	.4951	.4952
2.6	.4953	.4955	.4956	.4957	.4959	.4960	.4961	.4962	.4963	.4964
2.7	.4965	.4966	.4967	.4968	.4969	.4970	.4971	.4972	.4973	.4974
2.8	.4974	.4975	.4976	.4977	.4977	.4978	.4979	.4979	.4980	.4981
2.9	.4981	.4982	.4982	.4983	.4984	.4984	.4985	.4985	.4986	.4986
3.0	.4987	.4987	.4987	.4988	.4988	.4989	.4989.	.4989	.4990	.4990

B.4 STUDENT'S-*t* DISTRIBUTION

The first column lists the number of degrees of freedom (v). The headings of the other columns give probabilities (P) for t to exceed the entry value. Use symmetry for negative t values.

v \ P	.10	.05	.025	.01	.005
1	3.078	6.314	12.706	31.821	63.657
2	1.886	2.920	4.303	6.965	9.925
3	1.638	2.353	3.182	4.541	5.841
4	1.533	2.132	2.776	3.747	4.604
5	1.476	2.015	2.571	3.365	4.032
6	1.440	1.943	2.447	3.143	3.707
7	1.415	1.895	2.365	2.998	3.499
8	1.397	1.860	2.306	2.896	3.355
9	1.383	1.833	2.262	2.821	3.250
10	1.372	1.812	2.228	2.764	3.169
11	1.363	1.796	2.201	2.718	3.106
12	1.356	1.782	2.179	2.681	3.055
13	1.350	1.771	2.160	2.650	3.012
14	1.345	1.761	2.145	2.624	2.977
15	1.341	1.753	2.131	2.602	2.947
16	1.337	1.746	2.120	2.583	2.921
17	1.333	1.740	2.110	2.567	2.898
18	1.330	1.734	2.101	2.552	2.878
19	1.328	1.729	2.093	2.539	2.861
20	1.325	1.725	2.086	2.528	2.845
21	1.323	1.721	2.080	2.518	2.831
22	1.321	1.717	2.074	2.508	2.819
23	1.319	1.714	2.069	2.500	2.807
24	1.318	1.711	2.064	2.492	2.797
25	1.316	1.708	2.060	2.485	2.787
26	1.315	1.706	2.056	2.479	2.779
27	1.314	1.703	2.052	2.473	2.771
28	1.313	1.701	2.048	2.467	2.763
29	1.311	1.699	2.045	2.462	2.756
30	1.310	1.697	2.042	2.457	2.750
40	1.303	1.684	2.021	2.423	2.704
60	1.296	1.671	2.000	2.390	2.660
120	1.289	1.658	1.980	2.358	2.617
∞	1.282	1.645	1.960	2.326	2.576

CATALOGUE OF PROGRAMS AVAILABLE WITH BOOKS 1, 2 AND 3

PROGRAMS AVAILABLE WITH BOOK 1

Charts and tables

Descriptive programs
1. Frequency distributions
2. Relative frequency distributions
3. Cumulative frequency distributions
4. Qualitative, quantitative, discrete and continuous variables
5. Pictograms
6. Pie charts
7. Bar charts
8. Histograms
9. Polygons

Interactive programs
10. Frequency distributions using data supplied by the computer
11. Frequency distributions using data supplied by the user
12. Frequency distributions using previously saved data
13. Histograms
14. Polygons

Defining averages

Descriptive programs
15. The mode
16. The median
17. The mean

Interactive programs
18. Program description
19. Defining averages with data supplied by the computer
20. Defining averages with data supplied by the user

Comparing distributions

Descriptive programs
21. Outline of the program's example
22. Adding a constant to each value
23. Multiplying each value by a constant
24. Absolute and relative dispersion; the coefficient of variation
25. The Lorenz curve and Gini coefficient

Interactive programs
26. Program description
27. Policy 1: an increase of £X per week for everyone
28. Policy 2: an increase of X% per week for everyone
29. Policy 3: a combination of policies 1 and 2
30. Policy 4: changes selected by the user

Regression and correlation

Descriptive programs
31. Data generation in the regression model
32. Non-linearities and the regression model
33. Finding the line of best fit: regression and error minimization
34. The R^2 statistic

Interactive programs
35. Finding the line of best fit: regression and error minimization
36. Regression and correlation calculations
37. The correlation coefficient

PROGRAMS AVAILABLE WITH BOOK 2

Probability I

1. Set theory
2. Set theory example
3. Venn diagrams
4. Words and probability
5. Probability as a frequency
6. Subjective probability

Probability II

7. Combinatorial analysis
8. Axioms of probability
9. Conditional probability
10. Bayes theorem
11. Permutations and combinations
12. Independence

Random variables and distribution theory

13. Discrete random variables
14. Discrete random variables: dice example
15. Continuous random variables
16. Continuous random variables: archery example
17. Dice and histograms
18. Archery example

Special distributions I

19. Binomial distribution: theory
20. Binomial distribution: interactive
21. Poisson distribution: theory
22. Poisson distribution: interactive

Special distributions II

23. Rectangular distribution: theory
24. Rectangular distribution: interactive
25. Exponential distribution: theory
26. Exponential distribution: interactive
27. Normal distribution

27.1 Theory
27.2 Interactive
27.3 Normal approximations: theory
27.4 Normal approximations: interactive
27.5 Central limit theorem
27.6 Probability calculator
28. Approximations
28.1 Poisson approximation to the binomial: theory
28.2 Poisson approximation to the binomial: interactive

Bivariate distributions and expectation

29. Bivariate discrete distributions: more on dice
30. Continuous bivariate distributions: more on archery
31. Functions of random variables
32. Expectation
33. The bivariate normal distribution

PROGRAMS AVAILABLE WITH BOOK 3

Estimation I

1. Statistical inference
2. Estimators
3. Biasedness and efficiency
4. Central limit theorem
5. Properties of common estimators
6. Maximum likelihood

Estimation II

7. Biasedness and efficiency
8. Central limit theorem
9. Properties of common estimators
10. Asymptotic estimators

Hypothesis testing

11. Basic concepts
12. Construction and use of hypothesis tests
13. Small samples and unknown variance
14. Difference of two means
15. Confidence intervals

INDEX